This issue of GRAND STREET is
dedicated to the memory of
PAULO FREIRE, 1921–1997,
ALLEN GINSBERG, 1926–1997, &
MURRAY KEMPTON, 1917–1997.

FRONT COVER Tatiana Parcero, *Interior Cartography #36*, 1996. Black-and-white photograph on acetate and C-print, 10 x 8 in. The map superimposed on the hand in this work is taken from a series of Aztec charts or "codices," believed to date from the sixteenth century, that were made with native pigments on handmade *amate* paper by native scribes, after the Spanish Conquest, in order to supply the government with a wide range of information about Aztec culture, including local community structures and history.

BACK COVER Rubén Ortiz-Torres, *Los Payasos Diabólicos/The Devil Clowns*, Tijuana, Mexico, 1991. Fuji superglossy C-print, 20 x 24 in.

TITLE PAGE James Welling, *High Rollers Lounge, Pittsburgh, PA;* 1993. Gelatin silver print.

TABLE OF CONTENTS Marc Ferrez, *Entrance to Rio de Janeiro (View from Outside the Bay)*, circa 1880. Albumen print, 9 3/4 x 19 1/2 in.

Grand Street (ISSN 0734-5496; ISBN 1-885490-12-7) is published quarterly by Grand Street Press (a project of the New York Foundation for the Arts, Inc., a not-for-profit corporation), 131 Varick Street, Room 906, New York, NY 10013. Tel: (212) 807-6548, Fax: (212) 807-6544. Contributions and gifts to Grand Street Press are tax-deductible to the extent allowed by law. This publication is made possible, in part, by a grant from the New York State Council on the Arts.

Volume Sixteen, Number One (*Grand Street* 61—Summer 1997). Copyright © 1997 by the New York Foundation for the Arts, Inc., Grand Street Press. All rights reserved. Reproduction, whether in whole or in part, without permission is strictly prohibited. Second-class postage paid at New York, NY, and additional mailing offices. Postmaster: Please send address changes to Grand Street Subscription Service, Dept. GRS, P.O. Box 3000, Denville, NJ 07834. Subscriptions are $40 a year (four issues). Foreign subscriptions (including Canada) are $55 a year, payable in U.S. funds. Single-copy price is $12.95 ($18 in Canada). For subscription inquiries, please call (800) 807-6548.

Grand Street is printed by Hull Printing in Meriden, CT. It is distributed to the trade by D.A.P./Distributed Art Publishers, 155 Avenue of the Americas, New York, NY 10013, Tel: (212) 627-1999, Fax: (212) 627-9484, and to newsstands only by B. DeBoer, Inc., 113 E. Centre Street, Nutley, NJ 07110, Total Circulation, 80 Frederick Street, Hackensack, NJ, 07601, and Ubiquity Distributors, 607 Degraw Street, Brooklyn, NY 11217. *Grand Street* is distributed in Australia and New Zealand by Peribo Pty, Ltd., 58 Beaumont Road, Mount Kuring-Gai, NSW 2080, Australia, Tel: (2) 457-0011, and in the United Kingdom by Central Books, 99 Wallis Road, London E9 5LN, Tel: (181) 986-4854.

GRAND STREET

EDITOR
Jean Stein

MANAGING EDITOR
Deborah Treisman

ART EDITOR
Walter Hopps

POETRY EDITOR
William Corbett

DESIGN
J. Abbott Miller, Paul Carlos, Scott Devendorf
DESIGN/WRITING/RESEARCH, NEW YORK

ASSISTANT EDITOR
Julie A. Tate

ASSISTANT ART EDITOR
Anne Doran

ADMINISTRATIVE ASSISTANT
Lisa Brodus

INTERNS
Layla Hearth, Rachel Kushner

CONSULTING EDITORS FOR THE ALL-AMERICAN ISSUE
Susan Abrith, João Almino, Dan Cameron, Ronald Christ
Kristina Cordero, Ana Dopico, Clayton Eshleman, Jean Franco
Suzanne Jill Levine, Alberto Manguel, Gabriela Massuh
Carolina Ponce de Leon, Suzanne Ruta, Mark Schafer, Daniel Shapiro
Michi Strausfeld, David Unger, Eliot Weinberger, Octavio Zaya

ADVISORY EDITORS
Hilton Als, Edward W. Said

CONTRIBUTING EDITORS
Dominique Bourgois, Colin de Land, Mike Davis
Raymond Foye, Jonathan Galassi, Stephen Graham
Dennis Hopper, Hudson, Jane Kramer
Erik Rieselbach, Robin Robertson, Katrina vanden Heuvel
Wendy vanden Heuvel, John Waters, Drenka Willen

FOUNDING CONTRIBUTING EDITOR
Andrew Kopkind (1935–1994)

PUBLISHERS
Jean Stein & Torsten Wiesel

THE GLASS TOWER

Ever since he had arrived in Miami, after the veritable odyssey of escaping his native country, noted Cuban author Alfredo Fuentes had not written a single line.

For some reason, since the day he arrived—and it had already been five years—he had found himself accepting all kinds of invitations to speak at conferences, to participate in cultural events or intellectual gatherings, and to attend literary cocktail and dinner parties where he was inevitably the guest of honor and, therefore, never given any time to eat, much less to think about his novel—or perhaps story—the one he had been carrying around in his head for years, and whose characters, Berta, Nicolás, Delfín, Daniel, and Olga, constantly vied for his attention, urging him to deal with their respective predicaments.

Berta's moral integrity, Nicolás's firm stance against mediocrity, Delfín's keen intelligence, Daniel's solitary spirit, and Olga's sweet and quiet wisdom not only clamored for the attention that he was unable to offer, they also reproached him constantly, Alfredo felt, because of the time he was spending with other people.

Most regrettable of all was that Alfredo hated those gatherings, but was incapable of refusing a gracious invitation (and what invitation isn't gracious?). He always accepted. Once there, he would be so brilliant and charming that he had earned a reputation, particularly among local writers, as a frivolous man who was something of a show-off.

On the other hand, if he were to turn down invitations to such gatherings at this point, everyone (including those who were critical of his excessive talkativeness) would consider it evidence of inferior breeding, selfishness, even a false sense of superiority. Thus, Alfredo found himself caught in an intricate web: he was well aware that if he continued to accept the endless flow of invitations, he would never write another word, and if he didn't, his prestige as a writer would soon fade into oblivion.

But it was also true that Alfredo Fuentes, rather than being at the center of those obliging crowds, would have much preferred to be alone in his small apartment—that is, alone with Olga, Delfín, Berta, Nicolás, and Daniel.

So pressing were his characters' appeals and so eager was he to respond that just a few hours earlier he had vowed to suspend all social activities and devote himself entirely to his novel—or story, since he didn't yet know exactly where all this might lead him.

Yes, tomorrow he was definitely going to resume his solitary and mysterious occupation. Tomorrow, because tonight it would be practically impossible for him not to attend the large party being given in his honor by the grande dame of the Cuban literary circles in Miami, Señora Gladys Pérez Campo, whom H. Puntilla had nicknamed, for better or for worse, "the Haydée Santamaría of the exile community."*

This event, however, was not merely cultural, but also had a practical purpose. Gladys had promised the writer that she would lay the foundation, that very evening, of a publishing house that would print the manuscripts that he had, at great risk, smuggled out of Cuba. Alfredo, incidentally, didn't have a penny to his name and this, of course, could give him a tremendous financial boost, as well as help to promote the works of other important but still unknown writers less fortunate than Alfredo, who already had five books to his credit.

"The publishing project will be a success," Gladys had assured him on the phone. "The most prominent people in Miami will support you. They will all be here tonight. I am expecting you at nine, without fail."

At five to nine, Alfredo crossed the vast, manicured garden toward the main door of the Pérez Campo mansion. The scent of flowers swept over him in waves, and he could hear pleasant melodies emanating from the top floor

---

* Haydée Santamaría was the director of the government publishing house, La Casa de las Américas, that decided which books would be published in Cuba.

of the residence. As he listened to the music, Alfredo placed his hand against the outside wall of the house, and the stillness of the night conspired with the garden and the thickness of the wall to give him a sense of security, of peace almost, that he had not experienced for many years, too many years. . . . Alfredo would have preferred to remain there, outside the house, alone with his characters, listening to the music from far away. But, always keeping in mind the solid publishing project that would perhaps one day allow him to own a mansion like this one and that could also mean the future salvation of Olga, Daniel, Delfín, Berta, and Nicolás, he rang the doorbell.

Before one of the maids (hired specially for the reception) could open the door, an enormous Saint Bernard belonging to the Pérez Campos lunged toward him and began licking his face. This display of familiarity from the huge dog (which answered to the name of Narcisa) encouraged similar shows of affection from the other dogs, six Chihuahuas who welcomed Alfredo with a chorus of piercing barks. Fortunately, Gladys herself came to the rescue of her guest of honor.

Fashionably attired—although rather inappropriately for the climate—in an ankle-length skirt, boa, gloves, and a large hat, the hostess took Alfredo's arm and led him to the most select circle of guests, those who would also be most interested in the publishing venture. Gladys, at once solemn and festive, introduced him to the president of one of the city's most important banks (in his imagination Alfredo saw Berta making a face in disgust); to the executive vice president of the *Florida Herald*, the most influential newspaper in Miami ("A horrible, anti-Cuban paper," he heard Nicolás's voice saying from a distance); to the governor's personal assistant; and to an award-winning lady poet ("A couple of serious bitches," Delfín's sarcastic voice piped in loud and clear). The introductions continued: a distinguished minister, who was a famous theology professor as well as the leader of the so-called Reunification of Cuban Families. ("What are you doing with these awful people?" Daniel shouted desperately from far away, causing Alfredo to trip just as he reached out for a famous opera singer's hand and fall instead directly into the diva's ample bosom.) Gladys continued with her introductions as if nothing had happened: a famous woman pianist, two guitarists, several professors, and finally (here Gladys assumed a regal bearing), the Countess of Villalta. Born in the province of Pinar del Río, she was an elderly woman, no longer in possession of lands and villas, but still holding fast to her splendid title of nobility.

As he was on the point of bowing discreetly before the countess, Alfredo sensed that the characters of his budding opus were again urgently demanding his attention. And so, as he kissed the lady's hand, he decided to search for the pen and paper that he always carried in his pocket, in the hope of being able to jot down a few notes. But the countess misconstrued his intentions.

"I certainly appreciate your giving me your address," said the lady, "but, as I am sure you will understand, this is just not the right moment. I do promise to send you my card."

And with that, the countess turned to the award-winning poetess, who had witnessed the scene and, apparently trying to help Alfredo, offered a suggestion. "Now that you've almost finished writing your address, why don't you give it to me? I do want to send you my latest book."

And instead of taking the notes his characters demanded (by now Olga was moaning and Berta screaming), Alfredo had no choice but to write his address on the piece of paper.

Trays brimming with assorted cheeses, hors d'oeuvres, pastries, and drinks were being passed around. Trays that, amid new greetings and inquiries, Alfredo saw approach and then disappear without ever having a chance to sample from them.

At midnight Gladys announced that, in order to make the gathering more intimate, they would all move to the glass tower. This elicited a very pleased *Aaah!* from the guests (even the countess joined in), and, led by their fashionable hostess, they set off immediately.

The glass tower, circular and transparent, rose at one side of the house like a gigantic chimney. While the guests climbed laboriously up the spiral staircase (except the countess, who was transported in a chair designed especially for this purpose), Alfredo again heard his characters' urgent cries. Imprisoned in Holguín, deep in the Cuban countryside, Delfín begged not to be forsaken; from New York, Daniel's groans sounded aggravated and menacing; from a small French village, Olga, sweet Olga with her pages still blank, looked at him with a combination of reproach and melancholy in her eyes; meanwhile Nicolás and Berta, right there in Miami, angrily demanded immediate participation in the narrative that he had still not begun. To appease them momentarily, Alfredo tried to raise his hand in a gesture of understanding, but, as he did this, he accidentally tousled the pianist's elaborate coiffure, and she in turn gave him an even more hateful look than Berta's.

By now they had all reached the glass tower. Alfredo was expecting the real conversation to begin at any moment; that is, they would finally start talking about the publishing plans and the first authors to be published. But just then, Gladys (who had changed into an even more sumptuous gown without anyone noticing) gestured with an elegant wave of her hand for the musicians to start playing. Soon the bank president was dancing with the wife of the executive vice president of the *Florida Herald*, who, in turn, began dancing with the governor's assistant. A college professor deftly whirled around the room in the strong arms of the opera singer, outclassed only by the celebrated poetess, who was now performing a prize-winning solo. Between the clicking of her heels and the frenetic undulations of her hips and shoulders, she careened over to Alfredo, who had no recourse other than to join the dance.

When the music ended, Alfredo thought that the time had finally come to discuss the central issue of the gathering. But at another signal from Gladys, the orchestra struck up a dance number from Spain. And even the most reverend minister, in the arms of the old countess, dared to venture a few parsimonious steps. As the dancing continued and the opera singer began to show off her high notes, Alfredo was sure he could hear quite distinctly the voices of his characters, now at very close range. Without interrupting his dance, he passed close by the glass wall and looked out into the garden, where he saw Olga, quivering desperately among the geraniums, begging to be rescued with silent gestures; farther away, by the perfectly trimmed ficus trees, Daniel was sobbing. At that moment, as the diva's notes reached a crescendo, Alfredo felt that he could no longer excuse his own indolence and, still dancing, he grabbed a napkin in flight and began desperately to scribble some notes.

"What kind of a dance is this?" interrupted the executive vice president of the *Florida Herald*. "Do you also keep a record of your dance steps?"

Alfredo didn't know what to say. On top of it all, the pianist's stare, suspicious and alert, made him feel even more vulnerable. Wiping his brow with the napkin, he lowered his eyes in embarrassment and tried to pull himself together, but when he looked up again, there they were, Nicolás, Berta, and Delfín, already pressing against the glass walls of the tower. Yes, they had gathered here from different places to pound on the windowpanes and demand that Alfredo admit them (infuse them with life) into the pages of the novel—or story—that he had not even begun to write.

The six Chihuahuas began barking excitedly, and Alfredo thought that they too had seen his characters. Fortunately, however, their barking was just one of Gladys's bright ideas (or "exquisite touches," as the countess called them) to entertain her guests. And entertain them she did when, following her steps and the beat of the orchestra drums, the Chihuahuas surrounded the Saint Bernard, Narcisa, and, standing on their hind legs, imitated complicated dance steps with Narcisa herself as the central figure. For a moment, Alfredo was sure he saw a sadness in the eyes of the huge Saint Bernard, as the dog looked over at him. Finally, the audience burst into applause, and the orchestra shifted to the soft rhythms of a Cuban *danzón*.

Berta, Nicolás, and Delfín were now pounding even harder on the windows, while Alfredo, becoming more and more exasperated, whirled around in the arms of the award-winning poetess, Señora Clara del Prado (haven't we mentioned her by name yet?), who at that moment was confessing to the writer how difficult it was to get a book of poetry published.

"I know exactly what you mean," Alfredo agreed mechanically, distracted by his characters, who were now struggling on the other side of the glass like huge insects drawn to a hermetically sealed streetlamp.

"You couldn't possibly understand," he heard the poet's voice counter.

"Why not?"

By then, out in the garden, Daniel and Olga had begun sobbing in unison.

"Because you are a novelist and novels always sell more than poems, especially when the author is famous like you. . . ."

"Don't make me laugh."

By now Daniel's and Olga's sobs were no longer sobs at all but agonized screams that ended in a single, unanimous plea for help.

"Rescue us! Rescue us!"

"Come on," urged the celebrated poetess, "stop acting so modest and tell me, just between you and me, how much do you get a year in royalties?"

And as if the screams coming from the garden weren't enough to drive anyone out of his mind, Nicolás and Berta were now trying to break through the glass walls of the tower, with Delfín's enthusiastic encouragement.

"Royalties? Don't make me laugh. Don't you know that there's no copyright law in Cuba? All my books were published in other countries while I was still in Cuba."

"Rescue us, or we'll break down the door!" This was, without a doubt, Berta's infuriated voice.

"They're all thieves, I know that. But other countries don't have to abide by Cuban law."

With their bare hands and then their feet, Berta and Nicolás were beating on the glass wall, while the screams coming from the garden grew louder and louder.

"Other countries will adopt any law that allows them to plunder with impunity," Alfredo asserted clearly, ready to abandon the poetess in order to save his characters, who seemed, strangely enough, to be gasping for air, although out in the open.

"So how are you planning to get funding for the great publishing house?" inquired the award-winning poetess with an ingratiating twinkle, before adding in a conspiratorial tone: "Oh, come on, I'm not going to ask you for a loan. I only want to publish a little volume of mine. . . ."

Somehow—Alfredo could not figure out exactly how—Berta had managed to slip one hand through the glass and, right in front of her astonished creator, turned the lock and opened one of the tower windows.

"Look, lady," Alfredo said curtly, "the fact is I don't have any money. As far as the publishing house is concerned, I am here to find out how everyone here plans on establishing it and whether I can get my books published, too."

"We've all been told that you are going to be the backer."

At that moment, Delfín slid down the tower and was now hanging dangerously by his fingers from the edge of the open window.

"Watch out!" Alfredo screamed, looking toward the window and trying to avert his character's fall.

"I thought we poets were the only crazy ones," said the lady poet, staring intently at Alfredo, "but now I see that novelists are too—perhaps twice as crazy."

"Three times as crazy!" proclaimed Alfredo, running to Delfín's aid at the window, just as Berta González and Nicolás Landrove entered the room.

Alfredo felt embarrassed to have Nicolás, Berta, and Delfín Prats (whose life he had just saved) see him surrounded by all these people instead of being at work with them; therefore, feeling more and more under pressure to remove himself and his characters from the scene, he decided to say good-bye to his hostess and to the rest of the guests instead of waiting for the famous discussion to begin. Followed by Narcisa, who was now intent on sniffing his leg, he walked over to them.

But a strange tension permeated the tower. Suddenly nobody was paying any attention to Alfredo. Worse, he seemed to have become invisible. In her tinkling tones, the award-winning poetess had just communicated something to Gladys and her friends, and they all made faces as if surprised or offended. Alfredo did not need a writer's observational skills to realize that they were talking about him, and not favorably.

"He'd better leave!" he heard Gladys Pérez Campo mutter in a low, indignant voice.

But even if he understood (albeit with some measure of surprise) that those words referred to him, Alfredo felt so confused that he was not able to absorb them. Besides, the words had not been spoken directly to him, although they were certainly intended for his ears. Gladys's good manners and social standing would not allow her to make a public scene, much less force one of her guests to leave. Therefore, still with the intention of rescuing his characters (who were now, for their part, completely ignoring him), Alfredo pretended not to have noticed and tried to blend in with the conversation. But the countess gave him a look of such withering scorn that the confused writer took refuge in a corner and lit a cigarette. But wouldn't it be a sign of very poor breeding to leave without saying good-bye to the host and the other guests?

On top of everything else, right at that moment Delfín Prats opened the door to the spiral staircase, and Daniel Fernández and Olga Neshein came in. Holding hands and not even looking at Alfredo, they joined Nicolás Landrove and Berta González del Valle, both of whom had already had a few drinks and were well on their way to getting drunk. Once again Alfredo felt Narcisa's tail brushing against his legs.

The five characters of his story (by now, at least, he knew that these people were worth only a story) took great pleasure in walking around the room, eyeing everything with a mixture of curiosity and calculation. Alfredo concentrated all his energy on trying to make them leave. But they just would not obey. On the contrary, they mingled with the most prominent of the guests, the true elite, introducing themselves to one another, bowing and curtseying and exchanging pleasantries.

From the corner where he was hidden behind a huge tropical palm and obscured by the smoke from his cigarette, Alfredo carefully observed his five characters and discovered that none was dressed as he had decided. Olga, supposedly shy and sweet, had arrived wearing too much makeup and a tight miniskirt; she was gesticulating wildly, making faces and laughing too hard at a joke that the director of Reunification of Cuban Families had just told her. Meanwhile, Berta and Nicolás, the paragons of "unshakable integrity" according to Alfredo's vision of them, were kowtowing outrageously to the governor's assistant. At one point, Alfredo even thought he overheard them asking for a small business loan to open a pizzeria in the center of the city. For his part, Daniel ("the introverted, solitary one") had already introduced himself as Daniel Fernández Trujillo and was telling the award-winning poetess such off-color stories that the old countess had discreetly moved to another seat. But insolence seemed to have met its master in the talented Delfín Prats Pupo. While downing a beer (his fifth? his seventh?) straight from the bottle, he mocked his creator, that is, Alfredo Fuentes, in a manner that was not only grotesque, but also almost obscene and ruthless. With diabolical skill, Delfín Prats Pupo imitated Alfredo, exaggerating all of the writer's tics, gestures, and idiosyncrasies, including his manner of speaking, walking, and even breathing. Only then did Alfredo realize that he sometimes stammered, that he walked with his stomach thrust forward, and that he was bug-eyed. And as he watched his favorite character mock him, he also had to endure more face-licking from the passionate Saint Bernard.

"The worst thing of all is that for all his pretensions and ridiculous posturing as a brilliant author, he has no talent whatsoever and can't even write without making spelling mistakes. He often misspells my first family name and writes it without the t," concluded Delfín Prats Pupo, so as not to leave any doubt on the matter.

And everyone laughed, again producing a strange sound like the tinkling of wine glasses.

Increasingly nervous, Alfredo lit another cigarette, which he quickly dropped on the floor when Delfín Prats Pupo, mimicking his every gesture, began to light one too.

"Sir, would you please pick up that butt?" one of the nearest servants reprimanded him. "Or are you trying to burn the carpet?"

Alfredo bent down to do as he was told, and, while in that position, verified that the peculiar tinkling sound was produced by the tittering voices of the guests as they whispered, glancing at him with contempt. He brusquely extricated himself from the Saint Bernard's legs, as the dog howled pitifully, and approached the guests to try to figure out what was going on. But as soon as he joined the group, the governor's assistant, without looking at him, announced her immediate departure.

Suddenly, as if propelled by a spring, the guests decided it was time to leave. The countess was carried away in her imposing chair, while most of the guests kissed her hand, which was now transparent (at least to Alfredo). The famous opera singer was also leaving, on the (truly transparent) arm of the bank president. The minister turned to go while keeping up a lively conversation with the pianist, whose face was becoming more and more shiny and brilliant. When the award-winning lady poet left with Daniel Fernández Trujillo's arm around her waist, Alfredo saw the young man's hand sink effortlessly into her translucent body (although Daniel Fernández Trujillo's hand soon became invisible as well, and both figures fused into one). The black musicians were also leaving, led by Delfín Prats Pupo, who jumped around among them cheerfully, producing the familiar tinkling sound, while mimicking the gestures of the writer, who could do nothing to stop him. Olga Neshein de Leviant left with a mathematics professor, their hands entwined. In the midst of this stampede, Berta González del Valle stuffed her handbag with French cheeses, and Nicolás Landrove Felipe carted away the candy, both of them oblivious to Alfredo's signals and the protests of the hostess, Gladys Pérez Campo, who, on her way out in the company of her Chihuahuas, threatened to call the police. But her voice faded away into an imperceptible tinkling.

Within a few minutes, the hostess, the guests, and even the hired staff had disappeared, along with the characters of the story, and Alfredo found himself alone in the huge mansion. Disconcerted, he was getting ready to leave when the thunder of trucks and cranes reverberated through the building.

Suddenly the foundations of the house began to move and the roof disappeared; the carpets rolled up automatically; the windowpanes, freed from their casements, flew through the air; the doors left their frames; the paintings came off the walls; and the walls, moving at an unbelievable speed, vanished, along with everything else, into a huge truck. As everything disassembled and packed itself (the whole garden with its plastic trees, walls, and air fresheners was already moving out), Alfredo saw that the mansion had been nothing more than an enormous prefabricated cardboard set that could be installed and dismantled quickly, and that one could rent for a few days or even a few hours, according to the ad on the side of the large truck in which everything was being carted away.

In a flash, the site where the imposing mansion had stood became nothing but a dusty embankment. Standing at the center, still perplexed, Alfredo could not find (it no longer existed) the path that would take him back to the city. He walked around aimlessly, thinking about the story he had never written. But an enthusiastic bark pulled him out of his meditation.

Exasperated, Alfredo began running, but the Saint Bernard, evidently more athletic than the writer, caught up with him quickly, knocked him down and began licking his face. An unexpected joy came over Alfredo when he realized that her tongue was indeed real. He pulled himself together and got up. Caressing Narcisa—who followed him faithfully—he abandoned the site.

Miami Beach, April 1986

Translated from the Spanish by Dolores M. Koch

Aphorisms

AND OTHER DIGRESSIONS

EVERYTHING GETS SMALL

The zoo, twenty years later. The animals are smaller. Some day, if this continues, we will enter the cage and step on the tigers.

TRAVELS

When we travel, the present is never totally there; it is almost a past, like an anecdote; that's why it feels nostalgic, and also happy.

SOLITUDE

When our body sleeps, in a hotel room, in an unknown city, we touch the bottom of solitude.

NOBODY IS COMPLETELY STRONG

Even the wolf has moments of weakness, as when he's on the side of the lamb and thinks: "I hope he runs away."

CREDULITY

Not because people flatter me am I inclined to believe them, but because I am always spontaneously ready to believe what they tell me. In the world of each conversation, good manners require that we believe what our interlocutor is telling us. And in romantic relations, how can we doubt a person who looks at us tenderly and seems to have so much trust in our credulity?

LIFE, FOR THE YOUNG

I

Wasn't there ever a moment in my life—and in yours, reader—at which everything was possible?

II

I once thought that everything was very little in comparison with the immensity of my life.

RULE

Your life should resemble a description of your life.

KEEPING A JOURNAL

The inconvenience of keeping a journal: to ourselves we document the futility of life.

If a boy thinks about women, he can leave behind not only toys but also the terrors of the inexplicable world he inhabits. For all the bad-mouthing men do about women, they should thank them for liberating them from their fears.

Life is about adapting to incoherence.

Frequently letters are more fragmentary than excerpts, because they are really part of an ideal whole, formed by the correspondence and by the conversation of the correspondents; for them, and only for them, their letters are not incomplete.

Optimism and pessimism are foreign bodies that the mind should reject.

The moment comes when lost opportunities no longer matter. It no longer matters if things are going well or not.

It's sad to discover some justification for an injustice.

In order to forget our real destiny, we are all actors in the drama of civilization. All of us, including the executioner.

FROM A DICTIONARY OF BIOGRAPHY

Gambetta: French politician who went up in a balloon.

OUR ROAD

There are only heroes on the road to death.

FROM AN ANCIENT SAGE

I

The idea that earthly pleasure must become, in hell, a symmetrical torment, was concocted during a night of love.

II

When we were children they told us how the lover's eyes clothed the beloved in divine perfection. We now know that all of us—even the most prim and tender virgins—are veterans of this battle, weighed down with resignation, tolerating our pleasant adversary's imperfections, warts, and bad breath.

A BETTER LIFE

How pleasant life would be if it ended a little before death.

Translated from the Spanish by Suzanne Jill Levine

AIMÉ CÉSAIRE

THE WAY THINGS TURN OUT

It's true the speculation of the birds of paradise no longer wilts
the flower of the compass card and when I open the cage of my eyelids
when I unglove my perched hawks and throw them in a release of
pupils where the pollen of hunger silently performs the high
miracle of fertilizing the sterile flower of hopelessness
(froth of words thrown carelessly amidst the flame of a silence
concretion only glanced from my left breast too vivacious
outgrowth of the most savage act of my toes
at my will dragging scraps of the world
at my will stranding weaker and weaker gasps
that I arrange very well in wisely defunct worlds)
justice to the landscape! it is him the crier him again
the road smiles at itself in the sunsets
the stones tame the raging sea
the crabs that are the suns of the sewers rebelling against
the order of public roads are suspended at the top of the ancient palaces
my hands pass to each other the shriveled hatchet of omens
The city? Void of city. The city? Void of eyes void of
nightmares void of memory void of indifference

SECRET SOCIETY

From the lagoon rises an odor of blood and an army of flies
that peddle to women the fraud of the jewels of menopause
the kingpins of crime installed themselves quite comfortably
on the passage of history whose epilepsy has never been
greater than in that time when each inscription is
an adventure whose every letter jumps in packets of cartridges
an affinity of dust leads to the weeks that are the grooves
of a guillotine before which the public prosecutor stands guard
in any case the elevation and fall of the body warn
constantly of the stage reached by the always difficult
digestion of geological avatars
we care none for the moles who swelled the earth with the
seasonal growth of insurrection
we care none for the sun it is a raped girl who no longer dares
go home takes the place of a counter-rain of sand and mud
whose offensive above the cities imitates the perfection of
indiscipline of the troops of the polarized light
nevertheless
in spite of the adenoid antelopes who gather together after
a long run in the dawn of palm trees made by the tears
under the beloved necks and that the sagacious hand of consolations
will never drive away

(no more than a superstition will bite into the beautiful tree
reserved for the axe of idolatrous hearts in spite of the blood

that paints the blocks and throws across its mask the
bouquet of premature flowers of a scalp)

wind
and knives of the constellations
let's exchange with the convex satellites
the helpful little salute
that we exchange with the ortolan of sunlit snows
for us only at the discrediting of fragile skylights from which the
antiserum often throws its unloquacious sky
the train of the lifeguards of the sea
on the rails of this valley dispatched whenever I want
to the bottom of the mulish gravel of unmarked catastrophe

Translated from the French by T. J. Anderson III

Black Beauty from Compton/Belleza Negra de Compton, Los Angeles, California, 1992.

Títeres/Puppets, Tijuana, Mexico, 1991.

Patria o Muerte, Venderemos/Sandino & Mickey in a Restaurant, Mexico City, 1991.

Ducktales/Patoaventuras, Mexico City, 1991.

Santo Niño/Holy Kid, Guanajuato, Mexico, 1991.

RUBÉN ORTIZ-TORRES

Rubén Ortiz-Torres has been border-hopping for almost ten years, documenting in his photographs, videos, and films one of the world's great cultural comminglings. Not only has he shuttled between his native Mexico City and his adopted Los Angeles, between Southern California and northern Mexico, but also between the white world of West L.A. and the Mexican world of East L.A.

As Ortiz's work acknowledges, the region's culture is so mixed up that no fence or police force can separate it. The states in the U.S. that are most adamant about keeping Mexicans out are all former Mexican territories, while the cities that most support the "English-only" campaigns all have Spanish names. The fact that there are millions of citizens of Mexican descent in the U.S. undermines clean geographic and national divisions, while the cultural borders within U.S. cities (between whites and Chicanos in Los Angeles, for example) are often more pronounced than those between Mexico and the U.S.

Thousands of American tourists walk across the border at Tijuana each week in search of cheap tequila and gaudy souvenirs, while until recently thousands of Mexicans would cross the other way every day in search of work. Greenbacks cross over for a discount, wetbacks for a decent wage; some have visas, others American Express, but all are consummate consumers and their esthetic interests eventually have an impact on the marketplace, yielding hybrid products and uprooted objects.

Cultural interpenetration can cause a blurring of nationality and identity, but, in the work of Rubén Ortiz, it brings into focus the common, colorful objects of desire and the cultural movements that spawned them. Bart Simpson, Batman, and the Power Rangers have become the most popular *piñatas* in Mexico; the Virgin of Guadalupe is perhaps the most common design on customized low-rider cars in East L.A.; and "California" architecture, a colonial style from the time when California was still part of Mexico, is the pride of the *nuevos ricos* in Mexico City. Ortiz's photographs document the visual icons of this funky trilingual mix in a cultural geography unhindered by borders.

KURT HOLLANDER

monsters & messiahs

MIKE DAVIS

Perhaps the goatsucker is Nature's revenge for what we have done to the environment.

SCIENTIST ON MEXICAN TASK FORCE INVESTIGATING CHUPACABRAS,
The Washington Post, *May 11, 1996*

The wild is predator. It is the unexpected and the unpredictable. It is also dream. The Tongva of Los Angeles, like other first peoples, made no ontological distinction between everyday animals and those that appeared only in dreams or at the end of vision quests. Their bestiary, for example, encompassed the *nunas-i-s*, dreaded creatures who survived from the time of the Ancestors, like the monster scorpion living in a cave at the eponymous Rancho El Escorpion in the west San Fernando Valley. There were also different species of were-animals—were-cougars, were-bears, were-sea lions, and so on—in whom masqueraded the spirits of the most powerful shamans. And, most astonishing perhaps, there was the great inland whale that lived in Big Bear Lake (in Tongvan, "the lake that cries"), high in the San Bernardino Mountains.

The cougar on the cover of the *Los Angeles Times*, of course, is not necessarily less imaginary than a giant scorpion or a mountain whale. Our bestiaries, deprived of the Tongvas' continuous, intimate, and deep knowledge of their fauna, are animal cartoons based on random encounters and behavioralist clichés. Too often we equate wildness with urban disorder, and wild animals end up as the symbolic equivalents of street criminals. Or, conversely, they acquire all the psychopathic connotations of sentimentalized pets and surrogate people. The Otherness of wild animals is the gestalt that we

LEFT Mexican bank debtors' defender "El Chupacabras" spreads his cape after burning paper houses outside the Mexican Bankers' Association in Mexico City, May 30, 1996.

Enrica Lami, *Chupacabra*, 1996.

"El Chupacabras" struggles to keep himself chained to the gates of the Mexican Presidential residence in Mexico City, beside a sign that says, "734 days without solving the problem of overdue loans," February 11, 1997.

constantly refashion in the image of our own urban misunderstanding and alienation. Where nature is most opaquely unknowable, as it is in the "character" of animals, we intensely crave the anthropomorphic comfort of definition and category. Bestiaries, by definition, are hierarchies of allegorical fauna (including familiar species in their double role as social symbols) crowned by monsters. And monsters, which embody fears in sensual forms, are sometimes messiahs of consolation.

If Los Angeles's bad dreams in recent years have conjured monsters, like man-eating cougars, out of the city's own wild periphery, they have also laid out a welcome mat for monstrous tourists. In early July of 1996, for example, the famous goat-sucking vampire from Puerto Rico, *el chupacabra*, took up residence in the Latino barrio of Pacoima, in the northwest San Fernando Valley. A hybrid fad, midway between the hula hoop and the Devil in Salem, mass culture and mass hysteria, the *chupacabra* was simultaneously an avatar of poor people's deepest fears and an exuberant, tongue-in-cheek emblem of Latino cultural populism. I am not sure that the notoriously ill-tempered creature, with its bottomless appetite for *cabra, gallina,* and *pato* (not to mention the odd Doberman pinscher or two), would enjoy being called a messiah, but it certainly has been a lightning rod for immigrant anxiety. In a vast, strange city— sometimes more desolate than a desert and more dangerous than a jungle—the *chupacabra* has brought the reassurance of a familiar monstrosity.

Like Southern California's parched coyotes of the early 1990s, the *chupacabras* were brought out

of the hills and into the city by drought. Both in Puerto Rico, where the goatsucker first appeared in the town of Canovanas, twenty miles east of San Juan, in December 1994, and in northern Mexico, where scores of incidents were reported throughout 1996, there is good reason to credit local claims of a dramatic increase in mysterious attacks on livestock and pets. Puerto Rico is recovering from two years of drought and massive hurricane damage, while northern Mexico, together with the American Southwest, has been suffering through the driest period since the dust-bowl era of the 1930s. In both cases, as Puerto Rican veterinarians and Mexican agricultural officials have demonstrated in detailed investigations, there has been an unusual, drought-related hike in the number and ferocity of wild-dog and coyote attacks. (In Sinaloa, a zoological task force blamed pollution rather than drought: "There's no goatsucker, but pollution is now so bad that it's driving ordinary animals mad, giving them the behavioral trappings of crazed alien creatures.")[*]

From the beginning, however, folk culture was suspicious of "expert" explanations— "Who, after all, has ever seen a dog kill a goat like that?"—and preferred the agency of monsters and vampires. Indeed, the *chupacabra* may be an echo of the mythic bestiary of the Taynos, Puerto Rico's extinct aboriginal culture. At any event, its image underwent a fascinating evolution as sightings passed from the oral grapevine into the Spanish-speaking tabloid

---

[*] For the scientific opinion, see *The Washington Post*, May 11, 1996; Raymundo Reynoso, "La fiebre del *Chupacabras*," *La Opinion* (Los Angeles), May 26, 1996; *The New York Times*, June 2, 1996; and *Chupacabras* (San Juan: Redaccion Noticiosa, 1996).

press, then into prime-time tabloid television, before a final apotheosis as an episode of "The X-Files." Thus the original witness at Canovanas described an apparition "just like the Devil . . . four or five feet tall with red eyes and a hideous forked tongue." A month later, the *chupacabra* grew a horn, which a mechanic, attacked by the creature just before Christmas 1995, amended to long, spiked hair or fur. Its body was portrayed as a hideous combination of a rat and kangaroo. After the *chupacabra's* immigration to Mexico in early 1996, however, its image was remodeled yet again, as the bug-eyed rat face and punk-rocker hairstyle were replaced by bat wings and a space alien's head. In Puerto Rico, there had been intense speculation that the *chupacabra* was a mascot or pet left behind by extraterrestrial visitors; now, according to Mexican UFO experts, there was proof that the *chupacabra* was E.T. himself.

The Mexican left, on the other hand, declared that the *chupacabra* was actually Carlos Salinas de Gortari, the runaway ex-president, who "had sucked the blood of his country," and T-shirts with Salinas's visage, bald and big-eared, on the body of a *chupacabra* soon became a popular rage. So did El Chupacabras, a masked wrestler and social activist, who began to appear regularly at some of the nearly one thousand anti-government protests held in turbulent Mexico City during 1996. Elsewhere in Mexico, the beloved devil-rat-alien, Latino if not literally *raza*, was supplanting Mickey Mouse and the Power Rangers as popular icon: bars offered *chupacervezas*, food stands sold *chupatacos*, and mariachis sang *chupacarridos*. The delirious embrace of *chupacabrismo* by Mexico was, first and above all, a celebration of the national sense

of humor. Despite all the setbacks and infamies of the Salinas era, Mexico still owned its laughter. Yet, as in Puerto Rico and Florida (where a *chupacabra* panic broke out in the Sweetwater district of Miami in March 1996), there was also genuine terror. Scientists, government ministers, and even President Zedillo went on television to calm hysteria, while local investigators gathered irrefutable evidence of feral dog and coyote attacks on farm corrals.

In Los Angeles, the *chupacabra* craze was something of an antidote to the monomania of the Simpson trial. While O.J. was saturating English-language television in late spring and summer of 1996, the Spanish-language media, dominated by the huge Televisa chain, was covering *chupacabra* sightings in Sinaloa and Baja California, and debating whether the terror would strike in Southern California. In early July, two rabbits and a goat were found dead in a Pacoima barnyard. (Pacoima may possess some kind of occult locational significance since the Virgin Mary was widely believed to have appeared in nearby Lopez Canyon in 1990.) Although no one actually saw the *chupacabra*, there were tell-tale puncture wounds on the animals' necks and their bodies were totally drained of blood. Some people locked themselves in their houses and refused to send their children to school. Others had trouble sleeping and were afraid to take the trash out at night. The majority, however, simply chuckled: Los Angeles had recently acquired a first-rate *futbol* team; now it also had a genuine *chupacabra* to prove its Latin-Americanness. Meanwhile, in the chaparral-covered hills above Pacoima, a pair of well-fed coyotes were howling their own delight.

WINDOWS

THE TREE

Seven women sat in a circle.

From far away, all the way from his town of Momstenango, Humberto Ak'abal brought them seven dry leaves he had found at the foot of a tree.

Each woman tore a leaf carefully next to her ear.

One heard the wind blowing.

Another, the swaying branch.

Another, the beating wings of birds.

Another said it was raining in her ear.

Another heard the running feet of a small animal.

Another, an echo of laughter.

Another, a wave of applause.

Humberto told me this and I thought: Could it be the dead leaves were whispering in these women's ears the memories of the tree?

THE LETTERS

Juan Ramón Jiménez opened the envelope on his bed in the sanatorium on the outskirts of Madrid. He looked at the letter, admired the photograph. "Thanks to your poems, I am no longer alone. I think of you so often!" confessed Georgina Hübner, the unknown admirer who wrote to him from afar. The pink paper of that first missive smelled of roses, and the picture of a smiling lady rocking in a Lima rose garden was tinted with rosaniline.

The poet wrote back. And some time later the ship brought to Spain a new letter from Georgina. She reproached him for his ceremonious tone. And Juan Ramón's apology traveled to Peru. "Pardon me if I sounded formal, believe me when I point to my old enemy, shyness." Letters continued to travel slowly between the north and the south, between the sick poet and his passionate reader. When Juan Ramón was released and returned to his home in Andalusia, the first thing he did was to send Georgina a heartfelt testimony of his gratitude. And she answered with words that made his hands shake.

Georgina's letters were a collective effort. A group of friends wrote them from a Lima bar. They made it all up: the photo, the letters, the name, the delicate handwriting. Every time a letter came from Juan Ramón, the friends got together, talked about how to answer, and got down to work. But with the passing of time, the coming and going of letters, things began to change. They planned one letter and ended up writing another, much more free-spirited and inspired, perhaps dictated by that woman who was the daughter of them all but unlike any of them and who refused to obey their dictates.

Then the message announcing Juan Ramón's trip arrived. The poet was on his way to Lima to claim the woman who had given him back his health and happiness. The friends called an emergency meeting. What could they do? Confess the truth? Ask forgiveness? What good would such cruelty achieve? They debated long and hard. Late in the night, after a few bottles and many cigarettes, they made up their minds. It was a desperate move, but there was no other way out. And they swore on it: they lit a candle in silence and all together they blew it out.

The following day, the Peruvian consul in Andalusia knocked on Juan Ramón's door amid the olive trees of Moguer. The consul had received a telegram from Lima: "Georgina Hübner has died."

DREAMINGS

At the end of her days Grandma Raquel was blind. But in Helena's dream Grandma could see.

In the dream Grandma was not so ancient, nor was she a bag of bones: she was a five-year-old child, one immigrant among many who were crossing the sea from far-off Belorussia. On the deck of the ship Grandma asked Helena to lift her up because they were arriving and she wanted to see the port of Buenos Aires. And in Helena's arms she could see.

Then Grandma told her she wanted to see her loved ones, and Helena flew off with her and Grandma saw them. One by one she saw all the people she had loved in her life: "It's been so long since I saw you!" Grandma cried as she flew.

After so much seeing, Grandma wanted a look at herself: "I want to see myself," she asked. "I want to see myself," she asked. "I want to see myself as I was."

And in Helena's dream Helena tried, but she couldn't.

Translated from the Spanish by Mark Fried

LOVE STORY

WITHOUT WORDS

I don't need silence, now that I have no one to think about.

ATAHUALPA YUPANQUI

I met Mabel by way of fashion, but it shouldn't be thought that I'm a devoted follower of the latest styles. Now and then, as everyone knows, it proves uncomfortable to be always swimming against the current, and one succumbs without further discussion to the idea of wearing one's pants a little baggier or slightly more tapered. But it's Mabel I want to talk about, not fashion. Mabel, so distant now in a hecatomb of memories and abandoned calendars.

She was the youngest of three sisters, all mute from birth, who managed a small business in a district of Santiago. They had set up a space for it at the end of a large drawing room, although, to remember it correctly, it must have been a *living room*, since all Chilenos have a *living room*—as they call the association of two armchairs, a couch, and a lowly table, come on in, don't stand outside, let's chat for a while in the *living room*, a quadrupedal institution conferring indisputable status upon the house.

A thick vermilion curtain isolated the living room from the section designated for receiving the public, and the first time I passed that boundary I felt as if I had crossed a threshold into another world, into a universe of compressed time, a peaceful atmosphere populated with miniature palms, ferns, lamps covered with enormous shades in deep red cretonne, round tables, and chairs that held your back perfectly straight. Now that I think of it—since memory exists only in relation to other memories—it could have been described as a Proustian atmosphere that had strayed into a proletarian neighborhood. It didn't glorify anything or anyone, but I venture to say that it was a Proustian atmosphere without tedium.

Mabel and her sisters made their living altering hats and ties. For very little, their three pairs of prodigious hands could be sent into action, and in the blink of an eye, a butcher's gaudy tie was transformed from the width of a paddle into a slender ribbon that just shouted for an Italian label. Furthermore, compliments of the house, they showed the obese, sweaty butcher how to correctly tie a Prince of Wales knot and, through signs, indicated that the triangular knot was out of date, vulgar, if not to say saucy, don't you know.

Others arrived with broad-brimmed hats in the style of Lucky Luciano and, after a couple of sure snips of the scissors, they handed back Tyroleans fit for the Chancellor of Austria. Coming to an understanding with them— especially Mabel—was never a problem.

They might not have been able to speak, but they could hear perfectly. It was only a matter of raising your voice a little, without creating a scandal by shouting, and of clearly enunciating each word—since what they didn't catch completely with their ears they understood with their eyes, and they responded by moving their lips delicately, using their hands for emphasis.

From the first moment, I liked that atmosphere of silence, and I don't mean that ironically. It pleased me and, for that reason, I began taking my ties to them one by one.

The two older sisters had the quick movements typical of those who are mute. Mabel, on the other hand, was very gentle. She moved her lips and hands with the tenderness of an accomplished mime, and the meaning of her words was measured in the brightness of her face. She had something that attracted me, and it wasn't love, of that I am more than sure. Nor was I motivated by any kind of unwholesome intention. No. It was the knowledge that Mabel belonged to the world of stable realities, to a sense of permanence suspended in time close enough to touch with my hands. Mabel was the charm that drew me through the vermilion curtain and, once I was on the other side, made me feel that life could have some sense of—how can I describe it?—safety. That's it. I felt safe on the other side.

When my stock of ties ran out, I took to visiting secondhand clothing stores and bought the widest ties I could find. I ended up with a few that were really dreadful: ties with pastoral landscapes (complete with cow), seascapes, national monuments dedicated to the illustrious victors of forgotten battles, sports stars, photographs of singers who had passed out of fashion before I was born. And what about the salespeople! They looked at me as if I were a madman sent from heaven on whom they could palm off every piece of moth-eaten shit in their windows.

It didn't take Mabel long to discover my ruse.

No man could have that many ties, much less so many with the select patterns I entrusted to the three sisters' skillful hands.

One afternoon she told me that I didn't need to ruin myself buying more ties, that, if I wanted to visit her, I could come simply to visit her. She told me this with her mouth, with her eyes, with her hands.

My life changed conspicuously. I stopped going to the pool hall where I wasn't doing too badly; by then, I was already one of those in the group who could be counted on to win a few dozen beers from some newly arrived yokel. Each afternoon, I left the office, taking a long detour to avoid running into my buddies, and turned toward the shop of the mute sisters. We drank tea with cookies, and became experts on many aspects of the neighborhood gossip, until the time came to turn on the radio. There, in silence, we devoured the tango broadcast, the slow, heartfelt words of another Mabel, Mabel Fernández, who offered us "a voice, a melody, and a memory" over the airwaves of Radio Nacional and, later, drinking a few discreet glasses of vintage wine, we followed intently the stories of "The Third Ear."

The sisters relied on a receiver Marconi never dreamed of. It was a large RCA Victor, with that profile of the little dog leaning into the gramophone, to which the great Pepe, the local electrician, had made a few additions, allowing for the connection of three sets of headphones of the kind used in old radios by doctors of the hearing-impaired.

The cords to the headphones weren't quite long enough, so the sisters were obliged to lean toward the receiver, adopting the same position as the attentive little dog, and I enjoyed seeing them wring their hands every time the villain was about to complete his wicked plan and sensing how they relaxed as the hero raced to save the girl.

Stories of Chicago gangsters during Prohibition, of the Wild West, with Buffalo Bill as the leading man, every possible version of *Romeo and Juliet*, the exploits of Hercule Poirot and Miss Marple, the stories of Sandokan the Malaysian tiger, not to mention those of Holy Week: the Life, Passion, and Death of OLSJC and his lads all traveled through the bodies of the three sisters.

Before long I had turned into a kind of evening boarder and, after a brief negotiation, they allowed me at least to provide the wine to accompany dinner and to bring the empanadas on Sundays.

Months passed. When we said good night, after listening to the *Stories of the Sinister Doctor Mortis*, Mabel always walked me to the door, and we would stand there for several minutes watching a few scattered cars pass, me smoking a Liberty, and her taking in the cool air. It was during one of these leave-takings that she indicated that she wanted to talk to me alone, proposing that we meet at noon the following day near the entrance to the German Linen store, where she had to pick up a few things.

And so we did. The meeting felt somehow clandestine, and I was embarrassed at the thought of being seen by one of my friends. As I imagined the comments at the pool hall, the jokes I'd have to endure the moment I went back to pick up a cue stick, and dreaded, above all, the possibility of ending up caught downtown, we ordered milk with vanilla and I asked what was on her mind.

She drew her chair closer and, moving her lips silently, spoke words that I understood perfectly in the brightness of her eyes.

She thought very highly of me, and it made her happy to have me as a friend—because we are friends, aren't we? She said she knew that she was not an attractive woman, yes, okay, perhaps not as ugly as some other women on the street, but she knew that she was thin and that she didn't know how to walk in a way that pleased men, and she knew also that I saw her not as just another woman, but as a friend. After hesitating for a few moments, she added that I was the first friend she had ever had in her life.

I took her hands in mine. The odd glances of the young men around us no longer mattered to me.

This was the first time that she had found herself out in public with someone who wasn't one of her sisters, and this first time felt good. Trust. That's what she felt with me. Trust. She repeated this several times. And because she felt this trust, she wanted to ask something of me and if I refused, thanks to that same trust, our friendship would not suffer the least harm. Her entire life had consisted only of being in the shop, in the house, going to the fabric store, having an ice cream now and then, and once a month visiting the electric company to pay the power bill. She was thirty-five years old, and in all of her life she had never done anything more than that.

"Wait a minute. You never went to school, for example?"

No. Her parents considered it sufficiently disgraceful to have three mute daughters in the house, and refused to exhibit them in the neighborhood; furthermore, in public school they would have been objects of ridicule— "you know how cruel children can be"—and the special schools were very far away in both distance and price.

"You still haven't told me what you want to ask."

For me to take her around a bit to see the world. Not every day, that was understood. A good-looking, respectable guy like me surely had other lady friends, a girlfriend perhaps. Not every day, once in a while, nothing more. For me to take her, for example, to the movies, where she had never been, adding slyly that perhaps one day I might be bold enough to invite her to a dance. Naturally, I shouldn't worry about expenses. She managed her own money and, if it was all right with me, we could split everything.

I was dumbfounded.

"You've never been to the movies, to the circus, to the theater?"

She shook her head and continued to watch me.

Yes, I told her, immediately. Inviting her to see a movie was something I had been thinking about for a long time but out of shyness had not dared to ask. Without letting go of her hands, I also told her that it wasn't at all true that she was an ugly woman, not only that, but I clumsily used the line that she didn't look thirty-five.

She looked at me affectionately, leaned forward, and kissed me gently on the cheek.

Mabel and me. In no time at all, we transformed ourselves into devourers of films in Spanish. We took over the Santiago and the Esmeralda Cinemas. We never missed anything with Libertad Lamarque, Mercedes Simone, Hugo del Carril, Amparo Argentina, Lucho Córdova, or Sarita Montiel. Mexican films turned out to be too weepy for her, except those starring Cantinflas, and after the show we gorged ourselves on *lomitos* with avocado at Bahamondes, and climbed Santa Lucía while pecking at paper bags full of peanuts. Mabel had never been a sad person, but thanks to our outings she became joyful.

Mabel changed in ways that weren't easy to perceive at first sight. Mabel changed to the complete amazement of her older sisters.

One day, she insisted that I go with her to the beauty parlor, where she had her long hair parted on the side cut short, "just like Brenda Lee," as the hairdresser confessed, then shortened all of her dresses by several inches. Another afternoon, she appeared covering her mouth with her hands, and only removed them when she stood at my side. She was wearing lipstick, and had a sparkle in her eyes she had never shown me before.

Mabel changed, and her change pleased me to no end. Perhaps that's why I decided to invite her to a dance.

Santiago in the seventies. Every Saturday you could choose from some twenty parties held by clubs or schools. Dances to raise funds for a home for orphans. Dances to collect points for some beauty-queen contestant or other. Dances to benefit the victims of the last earthquake. A dance to help the meritorious fire brigade. A dance to raise money for students traveling abroad — in other words, to Mendoza* — from this or that course at whatever high school. Dances.

I settled upon a place I knew had never been frequented by any of my old group. The Catalán Center. An old ramshackle house on calle Compañia distinguished by the observance of good manners and the Carreño etiquette handbook which all patrons were required to follow. Mabel was elated. Her sisters, who had not looked favorably upon our outings, worked like slaves to make her dress. For a week they sat hunched over the Singer, pedaling away, then, at last, Mabel. How could I ever forget her?

Mabel dressed in rose chiffon, shoes of the same color, and a small sequined purse in her hand.

Between dances we drank small glasses of punch, avoiding the brazen

---

* A town just across the Argentine border from Santiago.

types who offered us their bottles of smuggled *pisco*, and together chose a contestant for queen of the party who would be able to count on our support. I didn't give her a moment of rest, not a minute's pause, in order not to risk her having to confront some lout asking for a dance. I had never been much of a dancer and, as for Mabel, this was certainly the first time she had done it; nevertheless, if the band played a mambo, there we were; a two-step, let's go; a cumbia, a tango, off we went, doing the best we could. At about midnight, the band took a break and was replaced by records, and there we were in the middle of the dance floor with the Ramblers, Los Panchos, Neil Sedaka, Bert Kaempfer, Paul Muriat, Adamo, embracing, swaying gently to the castrato voice of Elvis Presley crying in the chapel. Mabel was sweating beneath her chiffon dress, and I could feel the hair gel sliding down my neck.

"You are beautiful, Mabel, very beautiful," I managed to say before feeling a hand on my shoulder.

I turned pale. It was Salgado, one of the guys who ran the pool hall.

"Now I know why you disappeared, my friend. You sure have kept this quiet! Well, be a gentleman and introduce me to your girlfriend."

I didn't know what to say, and Salgado, ever light on his feet, brushed me aside and took Mabel's hand.

"A pleasure to meet you. Guillermo Salgado, 'Memo' to my friends. And you, sweetheart, what is your name?"

Mabel looked over at me, her eyes open wide. She smiled.

"What's the matter, sweetheart? Did the cat get your tongue, or did this tiger you're with bite it off?"

Mabel stopped smiling, and with some effort I found my voice.

"Nothing's the matter. You've introduced yourself, now disappear and leave us in peace."

Salgado grabbed me by the arm. I had insulted him in front of his date, and he couldn't leave it at that.

"Is that any way to treat your friends? If your girl is mute, that's her problem. There's no need to get angry."

I broke his nose with one punch, which was a terrible mistake. Salgado was much larger and stronger than me. Still surprised, less by the punch than by the copious amount of blood staining his suit, he stood up, and in the midst of an uproar hurled a right that I failed to dodge and that struck me right in the eye.

They threw us out, making sure, of course, that Mabel and I left first while they tried to stop Salgado's bleeding. Painful rays of light flashed into my swollen eye, and I saw little more with the other, clouded as it was by tears from the fight and from shame.

Once in the street, I tried to apologize, and Mabel raised a finger to my lips, indicating that I shouldn't speak. She held tightly onto my arm, caressing my head. I don't know how she did it, but the fact of the matter is that while we waited for a taxi, she found her way into a coffee shop and came back with a bag of ice cubes.

In the taxi, she pressed my head to her lap and the bag of ice to my closed eye. I felt strange. I felt like a knight-errant, like a member of King Arthur's Round Table. I felt macho after all, and regretted not having enough money to say to the driver, "Keep going, and don't stop until I tell you to."

"Will you forgive me?"

"Shh!"

Mabel's dress was delicate. I could feel the heat of her body.

"Will you forgive me?"

"Shh!"

Her body was warm. Her hands ran through my hair. I felt the firmness of her breasts against my face.

"Will you forgive me?"

"Shh!"

I raised my arm. I put my hand behind her neck and drew her toward me.

At first Mabel sat still, her mouth against my mouth, surprised, not reacting, but when I pushed between her lips, when she felt my tongue between her teeth, she closed her eyes and we searched the most hidden corners of each others' mouths. We kissed endlessly, I don't know how long. I only know that we were interrupted by a discreet clearing of the driver's throat. When I looked out at the street, the world seemed empty and without meaning. A red light stopped us at a point in the city neither of us had ever been to.

"Let us off here. What do I owe you?"

We walked arm in arm, not making a single sign to each other in our intimate code. All we did was stop every few feet and kiss, kiss until we no longer felt the need to breathe.

We kept walking that way until we arrived at a small deserted plaza. Hidden in the shadow of an acacia tree, I held her tightly, and reached down with one of my hands. I touched her knees, her smooth, strong, slender legs. I moved my hand up. Her thighs tensed, trembled. I slipped my fingers beneath the elastic of her panties. I ran my hand across the surface of her buttocks, which were hard as stone, feeling the hair from her pubis brush against my fingertips, and the humid heat that betrayed her sex. Suddenly, I sensed that she was crying. It was dark, and she couldn't read the movement of my lips asking if she was upset. I was about to pull away, but Mabel threw her arms around me and willfully placed my hand between her legs.

It all happened very quickly. The hotel, the low lights, the invisible face of the receptionist, the feet of the maid who gave us our towels, the large bed, the mirror on the wall, the absurd music coming to us from hidden places, the useless telephone on the night table, the boxes of matches with the hotel logo, the chiffon dress floating on the chair, Mabel in the semi-darkness, her small breasts, her English perfume, her moan stifled by the pillow, my defeat in semen and sleep and, later, the fresh pain in my eye, stung by the sharp light of dawn, waking up in a strange bed, reaching for Mabel, who was no longer there.

Looking into the mirror, I saw that my eye was one enormous blue stain that seemed to cover almost a third of my face. Fortunately, it was early, and on Sundays there aren't usually many people on the street. I took a taxi to my room, confident that with the help of a piece of steak the swelling would diminish, and then in the afternoon I would be able to leave for a meeting in my secret world behind the vermilion curtain. But the damned swelling didn't go down; on the contrary, the eye began to discharge a milky substance. I spent the entire day in bed, in the dark, and the next day I called in sick at the office. With the help of a doctor friend, who diagnosed me with a thundering case of gastroenteritis, I obtained a three-day leave, which I divided between mustard compresses, smoking, and thinking about Mabel.

On the third day, the eye had returned to normal size, and in the afternoon, donning sunglasses, I headed toward the house of the mute sisters.

I was greeted by the oldest sister, who, as always, invited me behind the curtain. And Mabel? She offered me a cup of tea, pointing out that they had the best, Ratampuro, and cookies. And Mabel? She answered in signs that she wasn't there, that she had traveled south to the home of some relatives, that she had suddenly fallen ill with a bronchial problem, and that the country air was very beneficial in such cases.

It was a long afternoon. The two sisters suspended from their headphones. The tango broadcast, the Esso Reporter, the insipid RCA Victor dog that leaned without looking at me, a radio adaptation of *Murder in the Rue Morgue*, the soup with pork, the tortilla with celery and ground rice, the boiled milk, the vintage wine. And Mabel? No. We don't have the address. They are distant relatives. Only Mabel stayed in touch with them. No. She didn't say when she was coming back.

The second, the third, the fourth day. The same vaguely sketched answers. Well, what city is she in? We don't know. Only Mabel knows where they live. She didn't say anything? No. She said nothing about the date of her return. What if something happens to her? What could happen? Don't you at least know what province she's in? No. We've already told you that. . . .

I stopped going into the mute sisters' house. I confined myself to waiting outside the shop and searched like a spy for a sign of Mabel among the clients who came and went with their ties and hats.

Later, I didn't even go as far as the entrance to the shop. I enlisted some kids who kept me informed in exchange for a few coins. Nothing. Not a trace of Mabel. Nothing. Not a word from Mabel.

In the end, one adapts. One resigns oneself to having lost paradise. Giving up without a fight is not the worst punishment. The worst punishment is surrendering without having had the chance to fight. It's like throwing in the towel because the opponent doesn't show up; even if the referee raises the prizefighter's arm in the midst of yawns, a feeling of defeat lingers until it becomes resignation.

I went back to the pool hall, to the cue sticks, to winning a dozen beers from the first stranger. Salgado was there waiting for me, and we gave repeat performances of the broken nose and the swollen eye two or three times, until we ended up shaking hands, declaring that friendship had to be like that, hard-fought.

Mabel.

With the passage of time, I learned to forget her eye words, the measure of her adjective lips, the sharpness of her substantive hands. With the passage of time, time passed over my steps, and I filled myself with forgotten things that were forgetting me. The city of which I have spoken no longer exists, neither its streets, nor the mute sisters' shop, nor the ties as wide as paddles, nor the miniature palms, nor the Proustian atmosphere free of decadence. All has succumbed. The music, the dance hall, the dog leaning into the gramophone. Everything is lost, I lost it. The swelling around my eye disappeared long ago, but the bruise on my spirit remains, and something is missing, Mabel, something is missing, and that is why I walk through life like a crippled insect, a lizard without a tail, or something like that.

Translated from the Spanish by Garrett White

ENRIQUE LIHN

ORDER HAS WON OVER

Order has won over my house
the Comet heater which works to my surprise
wraps all the rooms in a warmth almost human
The electric system has ceased to be a Christmas tree in foul weather
As in an Impressionist painting
I am breathing in a diffused light
You won't see books turned down on the dining table or papers on the floor
my house has shed that abandoned air of public squares
little frequented
that air of bad life that has dogged me everywhere
My ladies, although bound to the second of the trilogy by a thread that is a sigh
have a key to this house with which I feel one through them
equidistant from all
and from these women who nourish that equidistance
All this calm, you see, is due
to the presence of death in my house

I ALMOST CROSS THROUGH THE SCREEN

I almost cross through the screen
of the mirror able to see
what cannot be seen:
the world as it would be
if reality were to copy it
and not the other way round
the mirror full at last
of its own nothingness.

THE CITY OF THE SELF

The city of the self should stiffen
when death enters it
All its bustle is as nothing confronted by nothingness
Whether they like it or not, the troubled travelers
who keep on fruitlessly
coming and going from the city
under the hand that now
turns to shadow everything it touches
Inertia itself, however, awakens
in the governor a hopeless hope
In the face of death he shies from capitulating
although he himself is a shadow touched by death
but a shadow of something, firmly bound
to an imitation of being alive

Translated from the Spanish by Alastair Reid

THE REPUBLIC OF
TRICKSTERISM

PAUL SEESEQUASIS

We were urban mixed-bloods. Shopping malls and beer parlors were our sacred grounds; as we reached adolescence in the '70s, the Sex Pistols and the Clash provided the tribal drums. Fallen between the seams and exiled from the reserves we were the prisoners of bureaucratic apartheid, of red tape and parliamentary decrees.

Our tribal links were obscure, our colonial banishment confirmed by the Indian Act.* White bureaucrats and tribal politicians alike were our oppressors. "We are heading toward self-government," proclaimed Tobe, the Grand Chief of the Fermentation of Saskatchewan Indian Nations (FSIN) as he shook the hand of then Saskatchewan Premier Allan Blakeney.

In his hands Tobe, the Grand Chief, held a paper promising tens of millions of dollars; but that money and power were destined for only a select few. The Grand Chief's vision was obscured by power and long-legged blondes. He denounced Indian women who married white men, while blond secretaries and assistants crossed their legs in his plush office at the FSIN.

Mary Seesequasis, a.k.a. Ogresko, was born on Beardy's Reserve in central

---

* The Indian Act, legislation that measured eligibility for benefits by "blood levels" and dictated which laws applied to Indian populations, was put in place by the Canadian government in the late nineteenth century. Under the Act, Indian women who married white men lost their Indian status and became white in the eyes of the Canadian government, as did their children. These women were required to leave their communities and their children were separated from their extended families. At the same time, non-Indian women who married Indian men became Indian in the eyes of the government. Although this law has since been amended, some of the Act's provisions are still in place.

Saskatchewan on January 20, 1934, the first child of Sam Seesequasis, of Beardy's Reserve, and Mary Rose Nahtowenhow, of the Sturgeon Lake band. Sam, my *nimosom*, danced through life with gentleness and humor and became a leader in the community. Mary Rose, my *nohkom*,* was large and became a bear when she laughed. She hunted rabbits, decapitated chickens, and farted in the direction of bureaucrats and posers.

They made love, had nine children, and seven lived to adulthood.

The Grand-Chief-to-be and his family lived downwind from my grandmother's farts. He was born the same day as my mother and they played together as children; they fell asleep infused with dreams of *Wesakaychuk* and *Pakakos*; they hid under the covers from the *wetigoes* and hairy hearts.**

But their lives were destined to take far different paths. Tobe was born mixed-blood; his father Cree, his mother white. But the irony and humor of being mixed-race was lost on Tobe. He would grow up as a mixed-race "pure-blood"; purer than thou and given to exaggerating the quantity of his half-cup of tribal blood, Tobe lived in denial of his white parentage.

The Indian Act enabled Tobe to imagine himself a pure-blood. With Indian father and white mother, he was allowed to stay on the reserve. In 1950, my mother met and fell in love with a white man, Dennis Ogresko, and because she was *hisqueau*[†], she had to leave the reserve.

The hairy hearts ran amuck in 1950s Saskatchewan; cannibal spirits plagued the small towns and hid in grain elevators. It was open season on squaws, wagon-burners, and mixed-breeds. By courageously proclaiming brown-white love, my parents challenged the humorless segregational values of the time. Unable to hide on the reserve they learned to bear the taunts and jeers with laughter. That love could exist between races offended all the pure-breeds; and by making love, Dennis and Mary parented two cross-breed mutts—my brother and me.

---

* *Nimosom* and *nohkom*, grandfather and grandmother.

** Figures in Cree folklore: *Wesakaychuk* is the Cree trickster, a figure known for surprises, wisdom, and foolery. *Pakakos* is a mischievous curmudgeon who lives in the woods and delights in scaring people. *Wetigoes* are cannibal spirits and are generally unpleasant. Similar to *wetigoes*, hairy hearts can be zombies, or just cruel, narrow-minded souls.

† *Hisqueau*, a woman.

We experienced childhood between the seams, spending summers on the reserve, winters in the city. We played without leashes; without pedigree, we learned to live with our genetic-mixture coats and our lack of papers. We pissed on the city trees, marked our traditional urban territories, and barked ferociously at the white poodles. It was the 1960s and my mother, now a registered nurse, worked at the Community Clinic in Prince Albert in northern Saskatchewan, where she healed the urban orphans and mixed-bloods who were now entering the cities in increasing numbers.

Tobe, the mixed-blood pure-blood, had grown up too. He became a tribal politician, a chief of the reserve, and a wearer of suits and ties. His hair was short and his speeches were long. He spoke of self-government and economic development, but his mind was focused on attending conferences and getting laid in hotels. With enthusiasm he joined Wild Jean's Indian Affairs Bandwagon and Wild West Show*; and with conferences here and there and blondes to his left and right, he lived the modern-day chief's delight. Tobe sold his Pontiac—the Poor Old Nechee** had thought it was a Cadillac—and actually bought a real Cadillac. He hired a blond chauffeur. But while Tobe played the colonial game, a revolution was brewing in Prince Albert.

Malcolm Norris was a Metis trickster†, a rigorueau, and a shit-disturber and activist par excellence: a cofounder of the Metis Association of Alberta in the 1930s and an urban activist who cut through the lies of white bureaucrats and tribal politicians alike. Fate had landed him in Prince Albert and, in 1965, he and my mother became friends.

As a rigorueau, Malcom Norris was hated by the hairy hearts and the cannibal spirits. They envied his power, his ability to turn into a dog, a bear, or almost any kind of rodent he chose. From Malcolm, I learned to see the evil spirits around me. I felt the disapproving glares of the police, farmers,

---

* Buffalo Bill's famous show of the same name first presented the "wild Indian" to the world as entertainment. Wild Jean is a reference to Jean Chrétien, current Prime Minister of Canada, who was once the minister in charge of Indian populations in Canada.

** Cree slang for a person, usually restricted to Indians and mixed-bloods.

† The trickster is a character that exists in the folklore of many tribes. Whether animal or human, he challenges, provokes, and outrages. Often misunderstood, and never fully understood, the trickster's role is to prevent people from getting too serious about themselves or the world.

tribal politicians, and store owners. They were everywhere in the city and their numbers were increasing.

The cannibal spirits and the hairy hearts ruled the cities and reserves. They fed on both Indians and whites. "There just aren't enough of us *rigorueaus* left to stop them," Malcolm once told me. "These evil spirits," he explained, "feed on souls that are empty, rub against their bodies, and penetrate the skin. Sometimes a person can repel them if he is strong enough, or he can call on a *rigorueau* to drive the spirit away. But most people succumb and the cannibal spirits continue in their goal to create a world of hate. A world in which they can proliferate."

Then one day, Malcolm was missing. Search parties were organized and the mixed-bloods and urban orphans looked everywhere, but it was the squirrels, the rodent friends of the *rigorueau*, who led us to him. He had been dumped into a grain chute and his body was badly beaten. While the crows cawed mournfully and the stray dogs howled their lament, our procession carried Malcolm back to our house. He was laid on a bed and a group of women healers worked with him; after a few days, his heart began to beat again. Time passed and Malcolm cracked a smile. "My spirit has tasted life again, though parts of my body never will," he said. True he was now paralyzed from the waist down.

But being confined to a wheelchair didn't slow Malcolm down. He wanted to take over the Prince Albert Friendship Center[*] and remove the metal detectors from the door. Those detectors beeped a warning any time someone without an Indian-blood status card tried to walk past them. He called a gathering of mixed-bloods and orphans, at which he spoke passionately about uniting all urban skins, mixed or full. "Burn your status cards!" he proclaimed. "And throw away your colonial pedigree papers. Don't let the white man define us. Let's define ourselves." The mixed-bloods and urban orphans from the streets cheered and, with Malcolm leading them, they grabbed trees as battering rams and forced their way into the Friendship Center as the suits and ties, panic-stricken, climbed out the back windows. Leaving in such a rush, the suits didn't have time to shred their Indian Affairs hit list or their sacred status-card membership rolls.

---

[*] A cultural meeting place and drop-in center for Indians and mixed-bloods.

The Republic of Tricksterism, where humor rules and bureaucrats are banished, was proclaimed. "All skins are equal" was the first constitutional decree and a pair of red drawers became the new flag. Skins from the street came in to help the social workers heal themselves and tribal lawyers were deprogrammed.

The Prince Albert Regional Tribal Council was in a panic. They passed resolutions and sent ultimatums to the Republic of Tricksterism, demanding that it abdicate power. "We are the chiefs," they reassured themselves, "the big white men in Ottawa say so." "Ah—go on," replied the Republic of Tricksterism. When even memos from the Department of Indian Affairs failed to dislodge the trickster upstarts, the Tribal Council called in its heavy: Tobe.

Tobe, now the second-in-command at the FSIN in Regina, arrived in Prince Albert with a hundred tribal goons. They were armed with baseball bats, dog repellent, and mace. "When we talk about self-government we mean it for us, not for them," Tobe proclaimed as the chiefs cheered, patted their beer bellies, and licked their fat lips in anticipation.

The assault came at dawn. Calling in the mounties, who donned full regalia and did a musical ride alongside them in honor of the chiefs, Tobe and the goons marched in a column toward the Friendship Center. But the urban animals, the squirrels, raccoons, and foxes, ran out ahead of the approaching army and barked out a warning to the citizens of the Republic of Tricksterism.

"We must avert bloodshed," Malcolm observed to the citizens. "Violence is the tool of fools. It is with humor and irreverence that we urban animals must survive. Let them have their building back; let them issue their proclamations with dead trees; let them have their dubious titles like national chief; let them become the media stars: we'll find our humor back on the streets."

And so it came to be that Tobe and his goons recaptured the Prince Albert Friendship Center without bloodshed. "These mixed-bloods are cowards," Tobe proclaimed. The joke was lost on him.

Malcolm Norris was captured by the tribal goons and brought before the Prince Albert Regional Tribal Council. "He must be punished as an example," proclaimed Tobe. "He has committed blasphemy and challenged our noble and sacred institutions."

"Spare him!" yelled the urban orphans and mixed-bloods but, as always, the chiefs were deaf to the sounds of the streets. On a Sunday, surrounded by a procession of goons, Malcolm was forced to wheel his chair to the highest hill in Prince Albert. There he was nailed to a metal medicine wheel, his arms and legs spread in the four directions. Malcolm died soon after, and his body was taken by the goons and buried in an unmarked grave. The mixed-bloods and urban orphans mourned. Crows flew high and cawed his name to the clouds. A wake was held, and for four days the memory fires burned from street-corner garbage cans. On the fifth day the crows told the people that Malcolm had been resurrected but that he had come back as a termite.

The urban people rejoiced and Malcolm, in his new life form, moved into the regional Indian Affairs building and gnawed at the bureaucrats' desks until they dissolved into sawdust. Having completed his job in Prince Albert, he found his way into a chief's pocket and made it to Ottawa.

Rumor has it that even today Malcolm, the termite, has led an army of termites into a certain national chief's organization where he is currently munching away at the legs of a certain national chief's chair. Meanwhile, with the retaking of the Friendship Center as another dishonorable feather in his war bonnet, Tobe ran for national leader of the FSIN and won the big chief position at that fermenting organization.

"Who better to speak the politicians' garble? Who better to hide the truth between platitudes of self-government and economic development than Tobe?" proclaimed the FSIN in their press release announcing his victory.

Then in May 1987, despite the opposition of the FSIN, C-31* became law. With the stroke of a bureaucratic pen, status was restored to those long denied, as if the government could, with a decree, instantly undo a hundred years of damage. "Hallelujah, we're Indians," was the ironic response of the mixed-bloods. Our hearts soared like drunken eagles. We donned our chicken-feather headdresses, our squirrel-tail bustles, and fancy-danced around the Midtown Plaza.

For my mother, a full-blood Cree woman, the seemingly gracious

---

* In 1987, the Canadian government, under pressure from Indian and mixed-blood women, finally changed the Indian Act's provisions on mixed-race marriages.

convening of status was a double irony that could be dealt with only with humor. In the FSIN offices, Tobe, the mixed-blood pure-blood, and his Indiancrats, were having a bad day. They grumbled, drank double shots of rye, and hit their blond secretaries.

But C-31 was only a temporary irritation for Tobe. He remained focused on his career. He wore blinders whenever he entered the city so as not to see the urban orphans. He talked about First Nations as if the cities did not exist. He became bloated with his power and gained weight by the hour. As the Honorable Heap Big Chief, he increased his salary and his belly respectively. Meanwhile Mary Seesequasis moved to Saskatoon and worked at the 20th Street Community Clinic where she administered to the mixed-bloods, the whores, dykes, queers, street people: everyone.

"We are not victims. We are survivors," was the motto she lived by. Tobe was a survivor too, but in a more dangerous game. My mother saw the Indian Act as a bad joke. Tobe embraced it as a career. His sense of humor was lost in the shuffle of colonial cards and his heart was hardened by the cannibal spirits.

JUAN CAMERON

MARY BETH LACEY DREAMS OF BEING CHRISTINE CAGNEY

Lacey   Eurydice   is not Cagney
so New York from the sky is not the New York sky
and a simple outrage can blind it
But the sky of New York is not eternal   Eurydice
It turns and does not stay over New York

Lacey cannot be Cagney
She's not a sergeant   doesn't have seniority   couldn't
even get her own gun out of the holster
and the yankee bandits flow by like the river
that goes to end in the sea which is the electric chair
and this life   Eurydice   is not your life

As a loner   Eurydice   you fall short as policewoman
weeping over New York with lead
you fall short in weeping   Eurydice
Don't live that myth   your fire will be
extinguished in the Manhattan sky
To help you to feel   Eurydice
turn off the TV
                              go to sleep.

Last night the war came to an end
Nobody knows how it began
Nobody remembers when it began
A schoolboy opened his notebook to some page
and wrote the word war
last night someone erased that word   a body
went down softly toward the snow
with a small bullet lodged in its flesh   another
shook off its wound and walked slowly away
not looking at anybody
not knowing where

LAST NIGHT THE WAR ENDED

The war   ended in silence
there was no truce no accord but forgetfulness
it dissolved early amid empty boxes of shells
daybreak
lit up rubble in the background

Last night the war ended
Nobody knows why   last night
the war ended

This morning in the assembly there were fistfights
some
argued over the honors
           the medals
                the title of hero
                     the photo on the cover

Last night
the war ended
last night
the war came to an end
It's going to be difficult to agree on anything

ever again.   *Translated from the Spanish by Cola Franzen*

2
CHRONICLES

ANACONDAS IN THE PARK

Despite the modernistic flash that tears into the intimacy of parks like a halogen informer and converts the chlorophyll of the grass into swells of plush shaved by the municipal blade. Meters and meters of an orderly Forestal Park "how I love you green," simulating a criollo Versailles as a backdrop for democratic leisure. Or as a showcase for the park as Japanese landscape, where the underbrush has been subjected to the bonsai shearing of the military cut. Where video cameras that the mayor dreamed up squeeze dry the saliva of kisses in the prejudiced chemistry of urban control. Surveillance cameras that idealize a beautiful oil-painting park, where blond children's locks rock in the breeze of the swings. Floodlights and lenses camouflaged in the flower of the municipal lapel to control the senile dementia that drools down the seats of the House. Old men with bluish gaze and poodle dogs cut by the same hand that scissors the cypresses.

Even so, with all this apparatus of vigilance, beyond the sunset bronzed by the urban smog. When the shadow falls far from the radius outlined by the streetlamps. Barely touching the damp quilt of the thicket, the tip of a foot comes into view stiffly driving its toenails into the earth. A foot that lost its sneaker in the straddle of hurried sex, in the paranoia of public space. Entwined extremities of arched legs and blotter-paper lips that whisper, "Not so hard, it hurts, slowly, careful someone's coming."

Down the path come couples hand in hand stringing orange blossoms as they walk along the well-lit road of legality. Nuptial prospects who pretend not to see the frottage of snakes coupling in the grass. Who say under their breath, "It was two men, did you see?" And walk on thinking that they'll warn their future manchildren off the parks and off those lone men who walk the night and watch the couples in the bushes. Like that voyeur who was watching them not long before. Watching them make love in the sweetness of the park because they didn't have money for a motel, but it was better than ever in the green outdoors, with that spectator who could not applaud because his hands were otherwise occupied, beating off, full steam ahead, sobbing out an, "Ay, I'm coming, please wait just a minute." Then she said to him, "You know I can't do it if someone's watching." But by that time, "I can't" was a whimper silenced by the heat and "someone's watching" the spice of Egyptian eyes swimming among the leaves. A dizzying abyss that engendered bronze pupils, that pair of eyes that sprouted from her at birth. And when the little bugger turned fifteen, she didn't try to warn him off the parks because she knew that those golden eyes were leaves thirsting for the park. So she stifled the warning. Her "watch out for the parks" would be like a synopsis of green gauze, like a hasty drawing of the curtain of his young foreskin. Like driving him to slip through the pebbles like an asp in heat, pretending not to, lighting a cigarette so that the man following him can ask for a light and ask him what's up. And push him softly into the bushes without waiting for a response. And there, in full dampness, set fire to the curly forest of his pubis, sucking those peppermint balls with his lizard's tongue.

Raising that kiss of fire to the pinnacle of his selenite petiole. And as the ribbon of cars and buses slips by on the slope, the boy gives in to the lassitude of his fifteen paper years that sink like boats in the drenched sheet of the lawn. And if the creaking of the branches tips him off that someone is watching, so what. He knows how hard it is to see a porno film in this country; he, too, has watched and learned the technique of parting the branches to join in the incestuous trinity of the parks.

Perhaps watching is being the accomplice in a murder, strangling the victim in the voodoo doll that spills its rattlesnake poison between your fingers. The scene being watched is reflected by the glassy iris in the replica of the glans, like a generous helping for the hunger of the observer. That's why the moisture of the park unites the kid in a perverse anonymity. That's why every night he crosses the canopy of its feathers and doesn't mind coagulating with other men who slither down the paths like lost anacondas, like red-tipped serpents who recognize each other in the urgent semaphore of their rubies.

Workers, clerks, students, or seminarians, they are transformed into ophidians who shed the dry skin of their uniforms to tribalize desire in an opaque rattling event. Something abject in their staring eyes seems to accumulate a Sahara, an Atacama, a saltpetrous salt marsh of dust that hisses in the parched trident of their tongues. A single silvery thread fringes their lips in a seminal drizzle, drool that leads to the central den of the nest garlanded in toilet paper that absorbs the teardrops. Nests for hatching condoms that gather in the meadows, like children wrapped in polyethylene, to ferment in the sun in the saffron fertilizer of the magnolias.

Parks at night blossom in the dew of solitary pearls, in rice rains spilled by circles of handjobs, like an ecology of passion surrounding the couple. Collective masturbations recycle childhood games in desperate maneuvers; the slide, the swing, the rocking chair, the twilight hiding place for brotherhoods of grown men, who bond, rudder erect, in the summation of their cartilage. So, hand to penis, hand to hand and to another's penis, they form a circle that collectivizes the denied gesture in a carousel of handling, in a "tag, you're it" of touching and pulling. A tribal dance in which everyone hitches his wagon to the midnight express, tracking the caterpillar that takes form in penetrating and being penetrated under the blurry foliage of the locust trees. A milky ancestral rite in the round mirrors the full moon, bouncing it off more timid centrifugal voyeurs, who palpitate in the tachycardia of the hand among the weeds. Night on the prowl doing moonlit rounds cut off like a lactic necklace by the police whistle. By the purple flashing of the siren that fragments buttocks and scrota, bloodying the party with its stroboscopic blink. The law drums its lightning blows on hollow backs to the safari rhythm of its powerful phallo-charge. In the thrashing, they try to run but fall to the ground cuffed by their pants, cupping the sexual gladioli still warm and unpetaled by surprise. But the flashlights rummage in the brush and whip the spines camouflaged in the cold velvet of the violets. The little novice trembling under the hydrangea bush pulls up the blue-jean zipper that bites into his pelvis (when he gets home he'll change his briefs). In a desperate flight someone zigzags between the cars on the slope and, pursued by bullets, reaches the bridge. With one suicidal

leap, he flies over the railing and falls into the river to be swallowed up by the water. The cadaver appears days later balled up in filth on the shore of the Parque de los Reyes. The picture in the paper makes him look like a snakeskin abandoned among the rocks.

Even so, the parks of Santiago continue to ferment like amusement districts zoned off by the pruning back of citizen desire. The parks are places where it becomes harder and harder to slip in a squeeze in a coupling of subjects subjected to the public eye who seek out the licking of darkness to regenerate human contact.

•

STEEL LACE FOR A PENITENTIAL PILLOW
A spiral shiver twists through morality when the topic of rape in men's prisons flashes on the impact of the news. The common cause of rejection completes the golden fecal spectrum of the report. And it is on tape that the act itself is repeated in the filming of the testimony that photocopies the secret. The smutty scene is reconstructed in the close-up of the mouth being interrogated on screen. As if the real penetration never came to an end in its variegated forms of expertise. The untiring search for seminal gems and vestiges through the medical speculum that acts as a legalized penis, opening with the spark of its forensic eye the dilation of the anal grotto of the body lying prone on the stretcher.

It seems as if collective subjectivity has recoiled, as in the Middle Ages, at the profanation of these holy places; the last stronghold of the intestine to safeguard the relics of manhood. A warm cavern that jealously protects the secret of the Templars in the damp felt of its sheath. The phallocratic mystery tattooed on its inverse wall, in a hermetic algebra continually retouched with gold by the backwash of its waste.

Unlike the rape of a woman, which takes place in the porno narrative of the dailies and is allowed to drain away like a natural outlet in the face of Eve's provocation of fragile male erotics. A certain patriarchal fraternity underwrites and promotes these practices, like poses and postcards less discomfiting to the Christian vision than the outrageous offense to the male tabernacle.

This is why defilement in men's prisons seems to be the most traumatic kind, with repercussions that could lead to suicide. But appearances are deceiving, "the boys of old used Vaseline too," and the fathers of the country no longer have any backyard to defend. So they risk it all on games of leisure won and lost, mounting one another, set free by their confinement. On the inside nothing is so terrible; you just clench your teeth, bite down on the lace of the prison sheets, relax your sphincter, and forget ideology. "Take down the barbed wire" and die in the saddle, because the hemorrhage of propaganda stigmatizes those who squeal on their brother's kiss. If Abel had looked the other way, Cain would have been his fag.

This is the law of those who live in the shadows where the sky is parceled out by bars. Shadows plow the soccer field in an eternal zigzag of comings and goings over the same footsteps, over the same hated cement they scrape night after night in a dream of flight. Thousands of eyes clawed by the bars await the buzzer announcing visiting hour. Or, in the worst case, the howl of the siren that startles the breast, the racing, shouting, and stampeding of the enclosure accelerated by an escape. Afterward the roll call and the searches do away with the sugar, the maté, and the snapshots of a woman turned sepia by the sporadic trickle of her visits. A woman swallowed up forever by the fatigue of procedures and files in the tedious archives of the courts. A woman as a Sunday promise, when the retention of her image could still be evacuated onto her portrait. Later the shadow of her breasts creeping along the wall would be made flesh by the snowy gluteus of the newcomers.

And so, day by day, many men cross the penitential portico that shuts with a creaking of iron behind their backs. Some birdmen, mute with Alcatraz fear, will have to pay for their apprenticeship, crossing a dark alleyway face down and dripping tears of whey into their crotches. Especially those who are brought in for rape; they pay for their crime with the same coin that falls perforated into the broken piggy bank of their own assholes. To the beat of the *cueca* drummed out on the brass of the cells that masks the shouting from the ears of the gendarmes who say "partying again in gallery four." A simulacrum of a *huasa* feast, a peasant rodeo of mounting and bucking. A din of push-and-pull, pants split and at half-mast, showing off the open-cut Andean ravine through which pass both cattle rustlers and those who fled at a gallop down the rocky road of freedom.

It might seem as if certain children's games of strength and violence were repeated in these jailhouse bacchanals. As if the bronze horse spread its wings, trapped between the thighs that are pinning it, in order to fly up and break the celibacy of the bars. A Trojan horse to enter, to find a Helen in the labyrinth of its innards and escape far away, investing the walled city of that body that is filling up with fecund pollen with the libertarian overflow of the desire for the outside.

Thus it is, then, that these ejaculative rituals lose their drama in the childhood evocation of hide-and-seek, piggy-in-the-middle, or an in-cold-blood slapping game, where he who resists must prove himself, the wounded intitiate of the gang. The rape of men in prisons would be a card game with a marked card for the novice. A tacit accord of anophagy where he pays the rent the first time around and then gets his with the next one to arrive. A system of carnal excavations that duplicate the network of escape tunnels. As if the technique of drilling were first exercised on the body, then in the up-and-down plowing of the belly of the drains to reach the filthy but free sky of the city. A topology of desperation that drills its libidinal emancipation in the mud. Ready to penetrate the brick with the ramming of passion, scraping, and sanding on the furrows of the back. With nails broken by the flailings of asphyxiation and strangulation caused by the lack of air in the narrowness of the subterranean tube. To gain centimeters on the earth's flesh

with blows to the groin, with the pulse of broken spoons, with pelvic thrusts on the bruised tips and heads of worms that soften in the silk of their foreskins the painful vertigo of impalement.

A friendly practice in which the urgencies of the body lead to a brotherhood of miners. Extranational expropriations annexed in the shared hole. As if the thirst for freedom were spread by seminal irrigation in the conduits of the body. A pact of sperm rusted by feces, like the wilting jasmine of a black honeymoon that smudges the barbs of enclosure. Nuptials that turn fatal if they are discovered by the penal eye, whether in the tunnel or in the cell. Both crimes receive their punishment in solitary cells, in years and months added to the sentence, in new escape routes like love letters drawn in the shadows. Other velvet strategies to give the slip to the dog, the reflecting lights, and the guards at the wall. The future projection of an underground as a clandestine marriage. Unions of sex and death not domesticated by the cloister, tearing their way out of the waxy tulles of their confinement.

Translated from the Spanish by Mary Ann Newman

UNLAND
DORIS SALCEDO

PAGES 74–75
Installation view, 1995
Carnegie International,
the Carnegie Museum
of Art, Pittsburgh.

LEFT
Untitled, 1995.

BELOW
Untitled, 1992.

Untitled, 1995.

Casa Viuda IV
(Widowed House IV)
(detail), 1994.

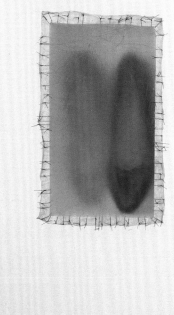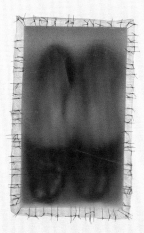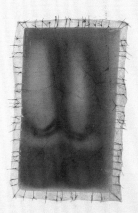

Atrabiliarios (Atrabilious), 1992–93.

DORIS SALCEDO

Imagine you're in Colombia, one of the most violent regions of the Western hemisphere (and possibly of the world), where military forces and jungle guerillas wage a decades-old civil war, drug lords lay waste to anti-drug personnel and each other's armies, and right-wing paramilitary squads carry out vigilante justice against whomever they deem guilty. Human-rights groups estimate that, as these campaigns have become increasingly fueled by terror and retribution, there are an average of ten political killings per day, of which six are non-combatant peasants or other civilians who got caught in the wrong place at the wrong time.

Doris Salcedo's art stems from her long-term commitment to seeking out and communicating directly with families of individuals (usually men) who have been killed in Colombia's most affected rural areas. Salcedo first came to international attention through her series, *Atrabiliarios*, in which shoes, alone and in pairs, are embedded in niches that she creates in the gallery wall, then covers over with a translucent "skin" of animal tissue. This physical yet porous separation between the viewer and the work creates a strangely tactile sensation that invokes the shoes' missing owners with chilling familiarity.

This close symbiosis between object and architecture is taken even further in Salcedo's *Casa Viuda* series. Literally translated as "widowed house," the series's title refers to the imaginary act of a home grieving for its lost occupants: in the works, chairs or doorways cling to bits of bone or the remains of a lace dress. Architecture and furniture are transformed into a compound entity, a quasi-life-form that is inseparable from the human lives around it.

A different kind of reality is embedded in the untitled concrete and wood sculptures that Salcedo presented at the 1995 Carnegie International. Built from simple pieces of furniture, these works feature both the implied violence of lives swallowed up by their surroundings and the more dramatic juxtaposition of intermingling forms with the hardened concrete that simultaneously bonds them together, cloaks them in silence, and threatens to burst their seams. In their exposed fragments and glimpses through surviving panes of glass, one still finds visible traces of the lives left behind—now encased in a prison that is as modest as it is unyielding.

DAN CAMERON

ALEJANDRA PIZARNIK

FIGURES AND SILENCE

Trembling hands send me into exile
Let me not ask for help
They want me to fall like night, to go and die
Let me not ask for help.

A DREAM WHERE SILENCE IS GOLDEN

The dog of winter bites my smile. On a bridge, I was naked. I wore a hat with flowers and was dragging my naked corpse that wore a hat with dead leaves.

I have had many loves—I said—but the most beautiful was my love of mirrors.

RESCUE

It's always the lilac garden on the far side of the river.
If the soul asks how far it is, the answer will be:
not here, but there, on the far side of the river.

To Octavio Paz

TÊTE DE JEUNE FILLE (ODILON REDON)

To André Pieyre de Mandiargues

the rain is music
the years, silence
one night passes
my body
    will never remember again

Translated from the Spanish by Suzanne Jill Levine

E.LUMINATA

Imagine a square space, constructed, enclosed by trees: with benches, lights, lighting cables, the concrete surface paved in squares and in patches the ground covered with grass.

Imagine this space contained within the city.

Imagine this city space at nightfall with its parts shrouded in dusk, though still clear.

Imagine this space desolate.

Imagine this desolate space just when the electric light comes on: the beams cast over its surface.

Imagine the entire square space illuminated by different beams filtering through the trees.

Imagine there any figure seated on a bench with eyes closed.

Imagine that figure seated on the bench with eyes closed and the cold spreading fiercely, unleashed.

Imagine that this figure is a woman with eyes closed, huddled against the cold, alone in the square.

Imagine that this woman is a ragged bag lady in the square, gone numb with cold.

Imagine her feet crossed on the ground and her head buried against her breast, hiding her face, with her eyes closed.

Imagine the trees tossed by the wind, revealing the lighting cables and in their midst that woman.

Imagine the city still, silent, only the night passing.

Imagine the woman seated on the bench with her eyes closed under a light.

Imagine the light on the woman's head.
Imagine a powerful light on the woman's bowed head.
Imagine her hand illuminated on the bench in the square.
Imagine her feet illuminated, curved on the ground.
Imagine the curvature of her back.
Imagine her curved.
Imagine her in other circular gestures.
Imagine her shut in.
Imagine the woman with her head lowered to avoid a light.
Imagine her completely curved body illuminated by a powerful light.
Imagine her head illuminated.
Imagine the nape of her neck shining illuminated.
Imagine the illumination of her closed eyes.
Imagine her fingernails illuminated on the bench.
Imagine her replaced under the light by another curved figure.
Imagine the scene constituted by a powerful light.
Imagine everything in tatters under that light.
Imagine her own rags exposed to a powerful light.
Imagine the imprinting under a light.
Imagine the extreme curvature imprinted under a light.
Imagine the extreme curvature imprinted under a powerful light.
Imagine the illumination of every electric light.

*

He asked me:—What is the purpose of a city square?

I looked with surprise at this man who had asked me such a strange question and told
him a little annoyed:—For kids to play in.
But his gaze remained riveted on mine and he said to me:
—That's all?
—Well—I answered him—it's a green space, it brings oxygen into the area.
But just when I thought he was about to change the subject, he said to me:—You are
sure that's all it's really for? Think a little harder. Then I really started to force myself
to recall the few times I had spent any time there, what I'd seen, and I replied:

—Actually, it's a place for recreation, even though lots of lovers come there too, now that I think about it, it's also full of lovers.

—And what do lovers do in the public square?

—They kiss and hug, I told him.

—And what else do they do there? he continued.

—Sometimes I've seen them touching their bodies, I answered.

—What do you mean by touching their bodies? insisted the other one.

—They caress each other, said the one they were interrogating.

—And precisely where does this take place? said the questioner.

—Usually they're sitting on benches in the square, although sometimes they're leaning against the trees but that doesn't happen as often. They touch by caressing each other while seated on the benches.

That's how they do it.

The interrogation seemed to come to an end, or at least the silence pointed to that. That's why, when the other one raised his voice, the one being interrogated was startled.

—And what else have you seen in the square? he asked forcefully.

The one interrogated hesitated a few moments before answering: —I've seen elderly people sitting on the benches too, especially when it's sunny there are lots of elderly people, he said.

—And what do the elderly people sitting on the benches do? How long do they stay there? asked the interrogator.

—They don't do anything, they think, but if somebody sits down beside them they try to strike up a conversation, maybe that's why they're always alone or else sitting in twos and threes, but never talking to each other, they only talk when their neighbor on the bench isn't elderly, replied the one being interrogated.

—But you didn't answer the whole question, said the other one. —How long do they stay there?

—For hours at a time, he answered.

—Who else comes to the square? persisted the one who was interrogating him.

He was running out of answers. He had to concentrate once again on his scant observation of the square until an image came to mind. That's why he said confidently:

—Beggars, some beggars show up there. He said that.

—Beggars? And what do they do?

—They stretch out on the grass and I've seen some doing that on the benches. They'll sleep face to the sun when there is any, or else if it's winter and it's cold, they'll cover themselves with rags or newspapers, said the one they were interrogating.

—And the others, are they bothered by their presence?

—Nobody goes near them and, if kids do, their mothers call them. Wherever they are a vacant space opens up. I think I heard once that it's against the law to sleep in city squares, said the interrogated one with a hint of enthusiasm in his voice.

—Who else, asked the interrogator, shows up there?

He thought he wouldn't come up with another answer. What else could there be in the square except for a few people killing time? Good God, who else goes to that place. Still he knew he had to answer, better for him at any rate, that's why he said: — Some kooks, a few crazies come there who stay as long as the rest but unlike the others, they talk to themselves or even make incoherent speeches—he was expressing himself more freely now—but the people, even if they keep away from them, they don't have the same attitude as toward the beggars, as if they know none of them's going to do them any harm. They don't show up that often, but it's not so unusual to see them there either.

—And how do you know they're crazy? asked the one doing the questioning.

—Well, he answered, it's easy: by their actions, by what they say. I don't know, there's something in their eyes that makes it impossible to mistake them. You can see right away that they're sick, they're off their rocker, they're some place else, they've got their mind some place else.

—Do you remember any one of them in particular? inquired the interrogator.

—No, no one in particular. They're like types to me, as if they came in a lump sum, he said, or maybe it's always the same one who shows up shabbier each time.

He did not know what else might come out if they went on like this. He was already astonished at having included the insane in the square since, in reality, he had hardly ever noticed them. His stopping in the square had always been a break between one thing and another and, as such, the place never commanded his attention. That's why it seemed to him now that it was a kind of unconscious observation that was surfacing and that he had seen a great deal more than he had realized. That's just how things were. But he was sure the questions had come to an end. But no. The voice rose again in order to say:

—All right, we'll go over it all again, this time in an orderly and coherent fashion.

Describe the square, but just that: describe it objectively.

It was absurd, absolutely absurd, that's what it was. He was not going to go on with this game, that's why he said:

—No, I won't do it, it's idiotic.

The interrogator looked at him and told him:

—Do it. That is all he said.

—It's a square space, answered the one they were interrogating—its floor cemented over, more precisely, paved in gray squares with a design in the same color. There are tall, very old trees and grass. Around the edges are set benches, some stone, others wood. The wooden benches are painted green and harmonize with the color of the lawn and the branches of the trees. Some of these benches are damaged from use, missing beams in the backrest or slats from the seats themselves. The ones in good condition are the stone benches, bound to be because of what they're made of.

—And the cables for the electric lighting and the lampposts? said the interrogator: you haven't seen them by any chance?

—Yes, that's true, replied the other one, there are cables and lampposts. The cables are visible in the tree branches and the lampposts are set around the square. They're painted green too. But they don't lend themselves to closer scrutiny. Their function becomes clear at night when the light's turned on.

—And what effects do they have when the light is turned on? said the one interrogating him.

—The square looks phantasmagoric, like something unreal, he said.

To give an example it looks like some scene in an operetta or a space for putting on plays. It's all very desolate then.

—Have you been there at night? he asked. I mean: have you stayed there?

—No, he said, I've never stayed there at night, I've only passed by when I've been walking somewhere else, but stay there, never.

—All right, said the interrogator. We'll drop this point for the moment, but tell me then, in the daytime: who comes to the square?

He had to play along. In this situation the right thing to do was not let anger or weariness get the better of him.

Obedience was what was called for.

That's why he calmly answered:

—I've seen kids playing there, accompanied by their mothers or nursemaids who keep an eye on them while sitting on the benches in the square. They talk among themselves, glancing from time to time at the children who mostly stay close by. Some of the very little ones fall down and give themselves a wallop on the concrete, then the mother or the person in charge of them gets up and consoles them until the crying stops. Sometimes they fight with each other which obliges the grown-up who's taking care of them to get up from the bench, interrupting conversation in order to separate them. The children like the lawn a lot, they roll across it, pull it up, and that way not only get their hands dirty but their clothes as well. Sometimes their mothers don't see them until the children come closer and then they say reproachful things to them. Some mothers knit and others even do embroidery and they carry food for the little kids in their bags. In the afternoon they get up, saying good-bye, and leave holding the children in their arms or by the hand. The exact time depends on the weather, but unless it's raining there are always children in the square.

He said it all at once, like a well-learned lesson, in a soft voice the way you would recite a piece of good literature, that's how he said it.

—But elderly people also come into the square, he went on, they're always bundled up, winter or summer. They're alone and looking to sit next to someone in order to strike up a conversation. The children are always the pretext, but generally the other person changes seats and that's why it's common to see two or three old people sharing the same bench in silence. They prefer the wooden benches, avoiding the stone ones. They stay there for several hours gazing from side to side. The women also knit and the men half-read the newspaper, since their gaze is distracted by the general panorama of the square. Frequently they go off, leaving the paper carefully folded on the bench.

He thought he ought to add a lot more about them, he could do it, but he did not.

—Lovers also come there, he said. Couples who sit on the benches holding hands. They talk very slowly and from time to time they kiss. Sometimes they're sitting on the same bench as some older person who, visibly annoyed, looks the other way. The couples laugh and the woman caresses some kid when playing brings him near. Now and again the square is also the setting for the end of some affair. They talk for a long time and sometimes the woman cries without hiding it. Then the man sits there, visibly embarrassed because of the others who are gazing at the scene and he hugs the woman, not as a loving gesture but to shield her from the gaze of strangers, as if he fears the others might blame him. At these moments the woman forgets the surroundings, but the man is hanging onto what the others might think of him. Generally the man convinces the woman to leave quickly and she leaves the square crying.

Other couples who meet in secret can also be observed. They sit on the benches farthest away, check the time often, and uneasiness conditions each one of their actions. These couples always seem to be on the point of breaking up. One of the two is there under compulsion, seeming to need a more intimate spot, but paradoxically there are lots of them in the square, like a prologue to something. They don't stay long, but they always follow a different rhythm from the rest of the square. They do not regard the other people, presumably for fear of their furtiveness being discovered. They lower their faces when a gaze crosses theirs. In short, they're there in spite of themselves as a way to dilute playing with chance. But some young people embrace without concealing it. They let themselves get swept over the threshold of their sexuality. These couples also remove themselves to the most distant benches, or they stretch out on the grass and their bodies rub against each other. They avoid the others' gaze and their hands slide subtly. But their faces betray them. You might realize that possession is imminent, that desire spreads in the square.

He interrupted himself. With lowered eyes he said: —I'm thirsty.
The one who was interrogating him replied:
—Later. Finish first.
—But not just young people spread their desire in the square, various ages are always present according to the different intensities with which they expose their shamelessness.
He thought that once again he still might add a lot more, but he decided to keep some things in reserve. Besides there was still a lot to say about the people in the square and his thirst was growing.
Just the reverse, he ought to synthesize more, save the maximum number of words, be sure about what he wanted to express.
—Beggars, he said, come into the square and stay there for stretches at a time. Sometimes they even come in groups. People are afraid of them and keep their children from going near them. They're threatening presences, not just because of the danger of aggression but also because of the chance of catching some disease they might spread by rubbing up against them or coming close. They don't beg. They even sleep there covered with rags or just newspapers that protect their bodies on freezing days. The bench doesn't matter to them, it can be wood or stone. They sleep very deeply and with their mouths open. Others come back to the place at different times of day, as if they had something to do and were returning to the square to rest.

It's possible that they go to some bar nearby. That's very possible, since almost all of them are drunks. They look wasted and stricken with age. The women keep their children away and those people don't even try to strike up a conversation with anyone. They recognize that they're set apart from the rest. But, nevertheless, they're rightfully there by virtue of it being a public place. Also it's well known, their disregard for the others and their enormous capacity for lack of connection with the surroundings. Frequently they also start rearranging things in the bag they carry and even take out some torn-up rags and bandage their legs which I've seen ulcerated and injured. If they're in the middle of that and some kid comes up to them, the mother or whoever's minding him quickly snatches the kid away, scolding him and explaining in a loud voice that never, but never, should he go near those people, who are dangerous, who are sick. Their ages are indeterminate, and well, they're always coming and going.

To the others who also ring the square he ought to add the students, the people on foot, but it would be endless. Unless it became absolutely necessary he would not do it.

The other's gaze incited him to continue, impatience was beginning to show in his eyes, that's why he said:

—Some crazies also show up and people maintain a different attitude toward them than toward the beggars. Not because these come near them, no, because pity mixed with irony and amazement are evident in them. As for them, they're characterized by their incoherent speeches that can be heard in various intonations. Some, even virulent. They're dressed like the beggars, but with more exaggerated touches. They don't look at the others either. Even though their harangues are crossed by insults of a public that never corresponds to the one listening to them. Life in the square isn't changed by their arrival. After a while they go away and the sound of their voices lingers after their figures.

—That's what I know about the square, I couldn't add anything else.

The interrogator got up from his seat and looked down at him, obliging him to raise his head, and said to him:

—You're tired, friend.

—Yes, said the one being interrogated.

—You'll rest for now, later, you still have some questions to answer. And raising the pitch of his voice he asked him:

—Who comes into the public square?

—Children, the people accompanying them, lovers, the elderly, a few beggars, occasionally some kook, answered the one they were interrogating.

—Describe the square, said the interrogator.

—Trees and benches, concrete squares, lawn, electric cables, street lamps, replied the other.

—How late do people stay there?

—Until nightfall, the last of the natural light, until the streetlights are turned on.

—When is the square empty?

—On rainy days, at night, in those circumstances nobody stays in the square, he responded.

—Come on, tell the truth: are the beggars so different from the crazies?

—Actually they're not totally different from each other, but the crazies are always talking, they seem worked up, but there's something they have in common that passes across their features, in the self-abandon they display, the one being interrogated answered wearily. The interrogator kept silent a few moments and his voice rose again:

—At what time does the electric light come on?

—I don't know exactly, but it is turned on at the same time across the whole city. When the square lights up, all the streets in Santiago are also being lit up. Something had definitely snapped. The questions were getting more and more trivial. But it was not something to get into a discussion about. So far as he could he was going to respond to whatever matter he was questioned on. Because something depended on that, or why else would the other man take that tone: the boldness of his gaze, the lack of facial expressions, the professionalization of this situation. Maybe it was to humiliate him or the prelude to getting at something significant and then he would be so tired that he would talk, beg, and ask for water, because his thirst would be unbearable by then. That's why he shifted his eyes swiftly when the one interrogating him said:

—I too have been there and that's exactly why you'll understand how all this could open up and lead one way or another to the inevitable conclusion. So that's why we're not building this thing up. Tell me:

—What have you seen when the light is turned on?

—I've seen nothing.

—Nothing? I saw the takes and, what's more, took them apart down to the point of disjointing them, frame by frame. It was an excessively long time while the beam of light struck my head, but even so I was there until I finished that job.

So that was it, thought the one being interrogated, that's where his attitude came from. It all got simpler if the guy had seen the takes. Which permitted him to say:

—Yes, I saw you and recognized you from the very first moment. When the camera shot you maybe your pose was different, but no doubt about it, it was a very typical gesture of yours upstaging that whole angle:

> when she was on the verge of falling and the arm of the man who stopped her was stretched out. That's how they were until he, who was bending over her, said some words to her, with her face wet with tears and it was a confession that E. Luminata hurled into the middle of the square at that man who was listening to her, enveloped in her gray dress, with her razed head down and her mouth almost in the ear of the man who was indeed prepared for this incident.
>
> Then they laid out the cables to set up the scene. Fused into one landscape and character, writing and medium, an error as well to praise it.
>
> What would he say:
>
> Nothing he might say would make the one held up stumble and, still, the simple familiar gesture of bringing her mouth close to the ear of a stranger could excite passion in others—despair in her—Imagine saying something that way to a perfect stranger.
>
> Laying her preference bare to another.
>
> It was an ongoing mistake because her voice was low and the cars that kept passing by drowned out her words. He half-listened and completed with his thoughts and desires what he wanted to hear.
>
> He changed words, suppressed whole phrases, cut important speeches, thinking them secondary. He could not extend himself to totalities. Not even heed her gestures, eager as he was to be consumed in their contents.

*

This isn't fair, I didn't see that scene.

—Don't hand me that line, said the man interrogating him. You were the only one nearby and that's why you broke her fall and then she spoke to you. Everybody knows that, just tell me what she said to you.

—It was something offhand, next to nothing. Really, it wasn't important at all, could've happened to anybody. It's hard to recall even, she was about to fall and

I rushed over to support her. I don't know what she said. Maybe she thanked me. Everybody's had something like that happen to them. Anyway, that's just why I can't recall her exact words, most likely because they weren't of any interest: a thank you, some conventional politeness, answered the man.

—But you remember the scene then? Let's start anywhere. Describe what happened, the one who was interrogating said to him.

—I was walking past there, he answered, suddenly I saw her stumble and knew she'd fall if I didn't support her. I rushed over and grabbed hold of her, even though I only broke the fall, because her body struck against the pavement anyway and I very nearly fell down myself. Afterward, I helped her up and went on my way.

—You stayed bent over her longer than usual. Why, asked the one who was interrogating him.

—Because I couldn't lift her, answered the man. I was in an awkward position myself, that's why both of us were struggling to keep our balance.

—The others came over? Anybody try to help you two? inquired the interrogator.

—Maybe, but I only managed to see the branch of the trees, the lighting cables. I didn't notice much else, really I didn't. From my position I saw only part of her face, then I lifted my gaze and caught a glimpse of all that. At that moment I couldn't visualize the others, answered the man. It was cold, he thought, it was dark. Actually that stuff about the tree branch was little more than a reflex, could be they weren't branches, or cables, or maybe it was the sides of her head that gave him that impression. From his position he managed to see almost nothing beyond the unobstructed view of her face which impelled him to images, but the other man had no way of verifying what he had seen. His statements were plausible. Whatever he said was probable.

He knew the tape was spinning somewhere. He had better be careful about what he said. Any contradiction was serious.

—But her eyes were full of tears, said the interrogator. You saw that, right?

—It's true, she was crying, replied the one they were interrogating.

—Why? asked the interrogator.

—It could have been pain from the fall, answered the interrogated.

—It could have been, said the interrogator, but it was not.

—And what was it then? responded the interrogated. Seems like you're the one who has the answers.

—You made her cry. It was something you said to her, you took advantage of her fall.

—She didn't fall all the way, I held her up. I lessened the blow somewhat, emended the one they were interrogating, and whatever I said to her didn't go beyond comforting her. Clearly she wasn't crying over what I said to her. She could have been crying from before and maybe her clouded vision made her stumble and caused this incident.

The interrogator then looked at him and coming closer almost whispered to him:

—Don't be so sure of yourself. I have all the time in the world. Sooner or later you'll stumble too, hit a pitfall, and then in tears you'll tell me what it was you said to her, how you took advantage of her, how and why you ran across to support her and I'll be tired out myself and I'll have already lost patience with you. You're pretty satisfied with yourself. Think that might have affected her?

—Look, said the one they were interrogating, what you want to know I've already told you and it's not a matter of time. It's true she cried but I have no way of knowing why. And my attitude has nothing to do with that. You want something else. Why not come out with it once and for all?

—What you've got to do is answer my questions, just that, he warned him. Keep that in mind, and then tell me: how long had you been watching her? How was it you got to her fast enough to break her fall?

—I was walking by there, answered the interrogated one, and her appearance caught my attention, it was a matter of seconds. I admit I went a little out of my way so our paths would cross and I could get a look at her up close. That was precisely what let me make my move fast. That small detour motivated by simple curiosity. Anybody in my place would have done the same. Of that I'm sure.

—Did she look at you before? asked the one who was interrogating.

—Yes, she looked at me.

—Why do you think so, persisted the interrogator.

—Because our gazes crossed, answered the one interrogated.

—What did you think then?

—That I wanted to look at her up close, answered the man.

—So you went out of your way then, asked the interrogator.

—Yes, at that moment I did.

—She tripped there and you came over and broke her fall, asserted the one who was interrogating him.

—That's how it was, he answered.

—But tell me: how could you see her eyes if it was dark?

—The streetlights illuminated the square. Besides there was a little natural light. Anyhow it was enough to see all that, said the interrogated.

—Or maybe you assumed she was looking at you or maybe she never looked at you because you were the only one who looked and the trees were protecting you and you were paying such close attention to her that when she passed nearby you came out of your hiding place in order to support her and then you told her something that scared her and made her cry. Maybe it was fear that made the tears stream down her face. It could have been that. At least that would be reasonable, said the one who was interrogating him.

—That's a preposterous story, responded the man. It was accidental, I already told you before.

—And then you thought the timing was right to approach her, the interrogator cut him off, because the innocence of the situation protected you. You were just somebody helping somebody else and that way what you told her was covered up because you had your mouth glued to her face and that's how you made your words almost imperceptible. And, although the two of you took longer than necessary to get to your feet, that was owing to the awkwardness of your position. Even those tears of hers could be explained by the surprise and the pain from the fall because her face, while she answered you, remained hidden by yours and the darkness in the square. It's possible, isn't that so? The interrogator had once more brought his face close to the man's and was speaking in a low voice, slowly.

—From one point of view it's probable. It strikes me as a good story, replied the man. But in the square that couldn't happen, I mean for somebody to be hidden by a tree and for her not to notice him beforehand. How could somebody have come into the square from any of its sides without having been seen? Walking under the lamps between the benches or cross between the bars of the fence in order to stay hidden in the grass? No, that wouldn't happen. It's all much simpler, I've already told you everything: our paths crossed under the light and that same light allowed me to see her and not let her strike the concrete.

He should not have spoken impatiently, not showed his irritation. Now the other one might get furious and lose his temper altogether.

That's why he added softly:

—I understand how you might think all that, especially if she cried, but the fact is that in the square what you say just couldn't have happened.

—You have lied from the start, said the one who was interrogating him, all that about the gazes and now that nobody could get into the square. It's too flimsy, all this stuff you're giving me. You're acting like an amateur. You know the difference between natural light and artificial electric light. Anybody can make mistakes. Camouflaging yourself is very easy.

—Under electric light? responded the man. No, that's not possible. The square isn't like other places. It's a circumscribed space, regulated. Once you get to know it well you recognize anything odd right off. Nothing is innocent: the benches, the lawn, the lamps, the cables, they all have a particular, well-defined dimension. Any point of view is going to take in the others. Daytime's something else, but at dusk or at night the movement is already programmed. The noise is programmed, the people.

—For just that reason maybe, the interrogator interrupted him again, you knew exactly how to go about it so as not to be seen and you took advantage of the only break to get near her, touch her, and speak to her, right there in the center so the whole thing would go unnoticed. But now then, let's finish: What did you say to her? It was starting all over again. It was like a circular scene rehearsed countless times. A scene gone astray, pointless. He thought about breaking this cycle, changing the point of view, switching to another subject that would unmask the weakness of its foundation. Start all over again but with another beginning.

Modify his role, change the tone, undermine his exhaustion.

But it was not possible, that's why he simply said:

—Nothing much, a few friendly words: that I was very sorry or something like that.

—How did she answer you, asked the interrogator.

—I don't know, I think she thanked me for the gesture.

—Where did the fall take place, continued the one doing the interrogating.

—In the square, in the middle of the square, replied the man.

—What made her trip, he asked.

—I'm not sure, maybe she stumbled from a bad step or perhaps it was a badly laid square of concrete or there was something on the ground she didn't see.

—What did you do then?

—I grabbed her fast as I could. Still her body struck the ground and I was on the point of falling too. I lost my balance because of the unexpectedness of the situation.

—Describe the position you two were left in, said the interrogator.

—She was on her side on the concrete with her head slightly raised. I had one arm resting on the ground and the other I put round her neck. Her head was practically underneath mine, but in spite of that the blow was softened.

—Could you see her face then, persisted the other one.

—Only part of it. Her profile really.

—What did she do then?

—One of her hands rested on the square's concrete and she raised the other to her head.

—Why did she do that, said the interrogator.

—Because she had something in her hand, something she pressed against her head.

—What was it?

—A piece of chalk, that's what.

—How did you see it? persisted the one who was interrogating.

—Because she was almost shaved bald and the chalk crumbled on her skull and fell to the ground. It even smudged part of her face and I felt it on my own hand.

—What did the others do then?

—I don't know, nobody came near us, answered the one they were interrogating.

—And why did she cry?

—I don't know, maybe she was crying before the fall, answered the man.

—Or maybe it was your words.

—I don't see why my words would have made her cry. It could have been the impact from the fall.

—And why did she have the chalk in her hand, inquired the one who was interrogating him.

—I don't know.

—But, persisted the interrogator, what do you suppose?

—That she picked it up somewhere, almost without realizing it, and carried it in her hand almost automatically.

—It's impossible, the other one interrupted him again. That can't be true.

—I don't know, I don't have the slightest idea as to what she would be doing with a bit of chalk between her fingers.

—That act was premeditated, so that's why the chalk couldn't end up by accident in her hands; you know that perfectly well and I know it too. What I want you to tell me is what she was going to do with the piece of chalk.

The man looked at him and then said:

—Maybe she wanted to write something, people do that all the time, it's something childish. At least that's my impression.

—It's true, replied the interrogator, undoubtedly she was going to try that. But in the end, the fall prevented her. Because you've said the chalk crumbled on the ground, isn't that right?

—Of course, I saw it myself and I even had tiny particles of it on my hand. I realized that afterward.

—And why do you think she crushed it against her head? Why do you think so?

—She could have been ill, she seemed confused because otherwise that action can't be explained. She seemed almost desperate or, at least, disturbed. Although after all it's not so strange; I've seen such things before. Some people are unpredictable, they have strange fixations on things.

—You mean the ones in the square: those are the ones who've got strange fixations—that's what you're saying, right?

—Yes, them, exactly.

—What makes you think so?

—It's the fault of the setting: that monotony, the same solitude, the craziness of the lawn, the straying of the light overhead.

—And the benches?

—The benches strain your sight too. Their amorphous shape, the discomfort, and even the parallel cables end up irritating your eyes, making them red. All loss of will power is pushed to the point of blindness. The benches invite people to occupy them. Movement in the square produces order and makes sense of its organization. It's a set.

The interrogator and the one interrogated silent.

The carefully placed tape goes on spinning.

Possibly a filmmaker frames them.

Someone transcribes the speeches.

—But it had rained in the square, asked the interrogator, you know that as well, right?

—Yes, but before, the previous day. It turned into dampness, the wooden benches, the grass, answered the one they were interrogating.

—And the cold?

—Sure, the cold, affirmed the one they were interrogating.

—You felt it?

—I was miserable, I was frozen stiff as a board, continued the one interrogated.

—And how did you manage to stand it, inquired the one who was interrogating.

—I walked fast, I moved around a lot, I crossed the square several times.

—Till you came face to face with her? asked the interrogator slowly.

—It was by chance.

—Chance?

—Let's start over again, said the one they were interrogating.

—Yes, replied the other man, that's the thing to do. Let's start over each time I want to. You should have understood it from the start. This always happens with beginners. It's a matter of patience, my patience. Go on, my friend: what did you tell her when you caught hold of her?

—I didn't say anything important, some conventional phrase.

—You were almost on top of her and her face was streaming with tears. I could say those words one by one but I want you to repeat them. I'd rather check the inflections of your voice, even copy your gestures. Do the scene over, reproduce that original. For just that reason tell me about the chalk again: how did she raise her hand to her head?

—You could never find out what was said, you're tempting me, it's easy to spot that, answered the one they were interrogating.

—But tell me about the chalk in her hand, insisted the interrogator.

—She crushed the chalk against her head, answered the one interrogated, smashed it at the moment when I broke her fall to stop her from striking the concrete.

—What did she write with the chalk? asked the one who was interrogating.

—I don't know, answered the other man.

—Or it could be you're the one who crushed the chalk against her head?

—That's crazy, responded the man.

—You did that, right? inquired the interrogator.

—What would I do something like that for? That's pointless. I'm getting tired of all this. What does it matter after all. What's it matter even if I did it myself. You want something else, you want me to tell you something else. Maybe everything would go much faster if you asked it once and for all.

—You think so? You really think it's unimportant? Look, nothing else interests me except verifying a few words, following a few gestures through to the end. By now the whole thing is over and done with. But answer me: why did you prevent the fall? It was scheduled. Why did you do it?

—I didn't want her to strike the ground. It would have been very painful. Maybe she'd have broken a bone, her head might have been injured. You know: the concrete, after all, anybody would have acted the same way.

—That's not true either. It was programmed, she'd readied herself for it. That's very serious: interrupting a scene, blotting out words, bending over her to talk to her, scaring her into changing expression. Making her lose her confidence. Tempting her, spurring her on to misgivings. That was your job. A slight shift of gaze, blaming it on the electric light. Are you satisfied?

—Yes, I did what I had to, it was my role, answered the one they were interrogating.

—That's true, but after the fall, without tears, without words, the gesture's what was asked of you, only that. But that's not how it was: you took advantage of the opportunity to make her confess, to detest, to take back what she'd said. You ruined the take.

—That's how it was.

—That's how it was, right?

—That's how, exactly how it was, but I insist that it was my role. It was bad writing after all. By rights the script shouldn't have included such a wallop. Not have her suffer a blow that way, after all's said and done, my action of catching hold of her was much more beautiful.

—She confessed, it's true, but she'd recognized the banality of her line. The forced reading. She cried, but not from pain, from the feebleness of her production. They couldn't swallow just anything. Not at all. Her body stretched out for nothing. Better to leave it like a rough draft. Like a rehearsal. That's what it was in short. Only that.

—But you went ahead and even out of the corner of my eye I could notice it. You were delighted with the fall. We were rolling and you didn't stop. You depended on reflectors, the light in the square wasn't enough. Camera in hand you were on the side opposite mine.

Really barricaded with your eye glued to the lens and your acolytes modified and synchronized the sound.

The interrogator rose and his eyes flared, he said:

—That my script was bad, that's what you mean?

—It was unsuitable rather, anachronistic, rough. Without technical effects only a univocal interpretation was possible. You confiscated the takes and in the darkness of the room I too was present for the projection of the rushes. I spied on your actions, your satisfaction, your eyes shining at the fall, waiting for the cut, the tinted curtain that did not fall. Your assistants were murmuring and there you were following the rhythm with half-open lips. You took the proof of the lines as real confirmation. You crushed the chalk between your hands and it crumbled until the lights came up. The titles fell and the word was not formed, however.

He said:

—The girl lacked style, that métier announced by her presence was just something she borrows from her private life.

Those present agreed with lowered heads.

He said:

—And maybe that's why I took all this time changing the editing. I cut and took moments that were different from one another.

—You follow me? Stop that blinking, we'll have to tear up the originals. They're worthless, they're badly put together. Doing it over is a major undertaking. The girl, it seems she's retired or at least that she's doing something else now. We'll have to spur her into taking up her old tricks. She had other projects livelier and bigger in scope. But it's ruined, with so much light it wasn't any good either for iridescence or the stable word.

Manipulated she took upon herself the tragic tradition. But it was simpler, much simpler than that.

—I prevented the fall. I took her confession and the tapes support that.

They advance, they curvet, they wear out from so much replaying. They spin them at each sound and also their volume is raised on the board. The technician sweats, modifies notes, interrupts, adds sounds: distorts.

Through technology he produces errata.

At last those originals are redone. Her fall is imminent and the press awaits.

The girl is properly posed. They announce the scene to the interrogator and to the one interrogated. They get their faces ready, the witnesses wait. The underpass is cleared to the point of being neutralized. The clothes are also right for the décor. The man takes the camera. The interrogated one confesses. Her voice also appears, slow, utilitarian, thick.

It's true, says the man, I did see that scene:

I saw her stumble and I rushed over. That was the only moment to get near her and make her give up the theatricality of the sequence.

I told her: if you fall now there'll be no possibility of redoing this stage. I told her: rub out the writing, it's no good, anyway you'll be criticized. I told her: get out of here, rest, think this over again. I told her: you're already considered one of the professionals, this fall is fragmentary, your speech is babbling. Redo the voice, correct the calligraphy.

It's true I elbowed aside the others who also rushed to see her, hear her strike the ground, make faces, try to steal a moment on camera. I blotted out these brazen tactics, I mugged my laughing at their tatters and I threw myself on her as hard as I could. They recognized me at once.

He gave the word to cut, the machines stopped just when the girl changed her voice to say for the nth time "where you going?" which she didn't actually say, but safely in my ear she said "it's a waste of time they reduced me to frames and me myself to a letter and those others to actions, it's too much, I only had a few thoughts, a couple of meditations, plots almost."

But it's like this:

They run around looking for the originals. The files are full of diverse proclamations put in order for their final cataloguing. They pile up on the tables. Stacks of papers that already are part of the past. Somewhere else the machine keeps up the same pace: they ink it and the man gives the order.

The square is really almost empty. The cold has set in. Numbed she curls up on the bench. Smiles.

She has chalk between her fingers. The benches are in lines, the ground, the tree trunks, the lampposts.

It will be printed in typography, in offset, a gray stain will serve as a cover.

The light in the square will come up. The show will go on.

Translated from the Spanish by Ronald Christ

OCTAVIO PAZ

ELIOT WEINBERGER *A few years ago, the municipal government of Mexico City approached Octavio Paz with a proposal to build a public garden whose gates and walls would be decorated with his poems. The garden was to be located in Mixcoac, where Paz spent most of his childhood and adolescence.*

Mixcoac, once a charming village on the outskirts of the city, is now largely a desolate, deafening, and polluted, anonymous corner of the spreading megalopolis.

Paz designed the verbal plantings for the garden, but, after visiting the site, decided it was impossible: Mixcoac had become another world. His poems, then, became stanzas for an imaginary garden to be built or unbuilt somewhere else.

•

STANZAS FOR AN IMAGINARY GARDEN

Four adobe walls. Bougainvillea:
eyes bathe in its peaceful flames.
Wind rushes: an exaltation
of leaves and kneeling grass.

Heliotrope runs by with purple steps,
wrapped in its own aroma.
A prophet: the ash tree. A daydreamer: the pine.
The garden is tiny, the sky immense.

The eight lines above describe a rustic village garden. A small walled enclosure with two entrances (the avenues Revolución and Patriotismo). Besides the palm trees which are already there, bougainvillea, heliotrope, an ash, and a pine should be planted. There should also be a small fountain.

This poem could be placed at one of the entrances to the garden, either as one eight-line stanza on the lintel or the pediment, or divided into two quatrains on each of the door jambs.

Rectangle of ease: a few palms,
jade sprays; and time flows, water
sings, stones keep still, and the soul,
dangling in the moment, is a fountain.

These four lines could be placed at the other entrance, on the pediment or the lintel.

Rain, loose hair and dancing feet,
its ankle bitten by lightning,
comes down to the sound of drumbeats:
the tree opens its eyes and grows green.

This poem could be placed inside the garden, perhaps on the fountain. I imagine a wall over which falls a transparent curtain of water where one reads the four lines.

COLOPHON

A crowded desert, a few palms,
plucked feather dusters, motors
rattling, a prison wall,
dust and trash, no man's land

Written after visiting the site.

In my ruins, this lush survivor:
you see yourself in my eyes, touch yourself,
you know yourself in me, and you think,
in me you endure, in me you vanish

Written remembering a certain garden.

SNAPSHOTS

They appear, disappear, come back, chirp in the branches of the tree of nerves, peck at now-ripened hours—neither birds nor ideas: reminiscences, proclamations;

comets—sensations, steps of the wind on the embers of autumn, sparks on a stalk of electric current: surprise, sudden rose;

shell abandoned on the beach of memory, shell that talks to itself, cup of whitecaps of stone, the ocean's bedroom, shout turned to stone;

slow rotation of the countries, wandering bonfires, sudden paralysis of a desert of glass, treacherous transparencies, immensities that burn and burn out in the blink of an eye;

blood flows through tall stalks of mint and hills of salt, the cavalry of shadows camps on the banks of the moon, tattoo of drums in the dunes beneath a planet of bone;

the melancholy of a rusted bolt, a beetle crowned king of a broken cup, butterflies keeping watch over a sleeping fuselage, the turning of a sleepwalking pulley: premonitions and recollections;

small rain on the eyelids of dawn, persistent rain on the devastated summer, thin rain at the convalescent's window, rain on the confetti from the party, rain of light feet and a sad smile;

a skull of quartz on the table of insomnia, the ruminations at dawn, the gnawed bones, scissors and drills, pins and knives, thought: alley of echoes;

speech without words, music more seen than heard, more thought than seen, music on the stalks of silence, blossom of clarities, wet flame;

swarm of reflections on the page, yesterday confused with today, the seen entwined with the half-seen, inventions of memory, gaps of reason;

encounters, farewells, ghosts of the eye, incarnations of touch unnamed presences, seeds of time: at the wrong time.

Translated from the Spanish by Eliot Weinberger

THE NIGHT OF THE COMET

LILIANA HEKER

For Sylvia Iparraguire

All we knew about the comet was that someone had plunged to his death to dodge its arrival, that its tail had luminously sliced across certain nights of the Centenary Year of the Argentine Independence, that, like the Paris Exhibition or the Great War, its path through the world had memorably illuminated the dawn of this century. The man on the wicker chair had spoken of a photograph he had seen, he couldn't remember where, in which several gentlemen wearing boaters and ladies in plumed hats were staring as if bewitched at a dot in the sky, a dot that unfortunately (he said) did not appear in the photograph. I had recalled an illustration in my fifth-grade reader: a family paralyzed by the vision of the comet passing through the skies. In the drawing the family members could be seen sitting at a table, stiffly erect, their eyes full of terror, not daring to turn their heads to the window for fear of seeing it again. (As soon as I said this, I had a feeling that the text referred to a Montgolfier hot-air balloon, but since I didn't know what a Montgolfier hot-air balloon was—I wasn't even sure that such a thing existed—and since I found it suggestive that I had attributed the family's surprise, whatever the real phenomenon might have been, to the arrival of the comet as early as the fifth grade, I didn't correct my conceivable mistake and everyone, myself included, was left with the impression that the comet was capable of sending people into shock, of leaving them frozen in their seats.)

We had a number of questions. How big did it seem when it was last seen? How big would it seem now? How long did it take to cross the sky? The man next to the table with the lamp suggested that, since it was as fast as a plane, unless one paid close attention the second it went by, snap, one would miss it. The man on the stool said no, that it rose over the river at nightfall and set over the western high-rises at dawn.

"That's impossible," said the woman leaning against the French door, "because then it would seem stationary in the sky. And something that seems stationary can't leave a trail on the sea or in the sky, anywhere." Since this seemed illogical but plausible, several of us agreed with her. What we couldn't agree on was the size.

"The size of the moon," said the woman in the light-colored armchair.

"Of a very small star," said the man who was putting on the tape of *Eine Kleine Nachtmusik*, and he added that it could only be distinguished from the star by its tail. And how long was the tail? The questions never stopped.

"My grandfather told us he'd seen it," said the man smoking a pipe. "He was in the courtyard, sitting on a three-legged stool," (I thought the stool was an aleatory detail and I immediately decided that his testimony was suspect) "and the comet went by, neither very slow nor very fast, like a scarf made out of light. No: like a scarf made out of *air* that was also light, I think he said." But, of course, this piece of information was simply too unreliable: given the age of the man with the pipe, his grandfather must have died long ago. Even if he hadn't made the story up (as the detail of the stool led one to suppose), who could swear that the grandson remembered the words exactly? And would he have been able to tell what was false from what was true? In fact, he had repeated the thing about the stool without lending the superfluous detail the slightest touch of irony.

But why were we to care what that grandfather saw? We had no need for grandfathers; our turn had come at last: it would cross the skies of our time. And we felt fortunate in those unfortunate days just being alive, still able to move around happily, still able to wait happily on the night of the comet.

Actually, that whole year had been the year of the comet, but since the previous week everyone's hopes had run wild. The newspapers predicted glorious events: this time it would pass closer to the Earth than at the beginning of the century; it would look mainly red; it would look mainly white, but would be dragging an orange tail; it would have the apparent size of a small melon, the length of a common snake; it would cover seventy percent of the visible sky. This last possibility intrigued us the most.

"What do they mean, seventy percent of the sky?" asked the woman drinking coffee.

"But then almost the whole sky will be the comet," said the man who had come with his girlfriend.

"Night will become day," (the woman lighting the cigarette).

"Better than day," (the man with the pillow on the floor) "as if the moon, with all its reflected light, were barely a hundred yards from the Earth. Low down, in a corner, one sees the black night sky, but all the rest is moon. Can you imagine? Solid moon." There was a silence, as if we were all trying to imagine a sky of solid moon.

"And how long will it stay like that?" (the man with his eyes glued on the woman who came alone).

"The comet is constantly moving. It will move on and the strip of darkness will become wider and wider until there's only a thin thread, a thin thread of light on the horizon that will then disappear and it will be night again." I felt a sort of sadness; I had only just realized that this thing which had once seemed out of my reach—like the boiling oil thrown by the women of Buenos Aires on the invading English troops in the mid-eighteenth century, or the Firpo-Dempsey match—was not only about to take place; it would also come to an end.

"But how fast will it disappear?" No one knew.

The woman with her back against one of the men's knees hit herself on the forehead: "Now that I think about it, no," she said, "it can't be the width. The comet will take up seventy percent of the length. Don't you see? The tail. It's the tail that will take up seventy percent. Like a rainbow going from here to there," (she drew a vast segment of a circle with her extended arm) "but ending before it reaches the horizon." She thought for a moment. "At a distance of thirty percent," she added, with a touch of scientific rigor.

That wasn't bad, though I still preferred the vast moon unfolded a hundred yards from Earth. And at what speed would that great arch of light cross the sky? That question—and many others—remained unanswered.

But we didn't feel uneasy. Uneasy we had felt at the beginning of the week, when the papers announced that the comet was already over the world. We had always imagined that we'd rush out into the street to greet its arrival. "Here it comes, here comes the comet!" But none of that happened. We looked up into the sky and saw nothing.

There were those with telescopes, of course. Those with telescopes made calculations and drew up schedules and strategic points. It seems that the brother-in-law of the woman caressing one of the men's ears, after consulting several manuals, had found the very best optical conditions: on the balcony of one of his cousins at 3:25 Wednesday morning with a telescope aimed at 40 degrees off the constellation of Centaurus.

"But your brother-in-law, did he actually see it?" we asked at the same time, as both the man and I played with the cat.

"He says he *thinks* he saw it," was the cautious answer.

We had heard of some people who had traveled to Chascomús or to a place somewhere between San Miguel del Monte and Las Flores, or of others who had hurried to Tandil, to a small hill close to the Moving Rock. But as we had not had the chance to talk to any of them, we didn't know whether these peregrinations had been fruitful. Through ads in the newspapers we knew that several kinds of charters had been organized, from a jet flight to San Martín de los Andes that included champagne dinner, diplomatic suite, sauna, and full American breakfast, to bus tours to several suburban areas, a few with traditional barbecue and guitar music under the comet's light. We didn't know what the results had been. But three very precise lines in a Thursday paper made us dismiss all those telescopes and nocturnal ramblings. And that's how it had to be. Because what we had always dreamed of, what we truly wished for, was simply to look up and see it. And that, the three lines in the paper said, would become possible on Friday night once it was completely dark; then the comet would come closer to Earth than ever before. Then, and only then, might it be seen as those men in boaters and those women in hats had seen it, as the grandfather on his three-legged stool and the bewitched family in my reader had seen it. Right here, by the river, on the Costanera Sur. And, in honor of that unique moment for which we had longed since our days of reading adventure stories and which, with luck, would repeat itself for our children's grandchildren, this Friday night, all the lights of the Costanera would be switched off.

That was the reason that waiting in this house in San Telmo, among lamps and stools, was something of a vigil. Every so often someone would go out onto the balcony to see whether it was already dark.

"No use going earlier," (the woman drinking wine). "We wouldn't see anything in the light."

And the man on the balcony: "No, it's not because of the light, it's because it won't come over the horizon until it's dark. That's what the paper says."

But at what time exactly? We didn't know that either. Darkness isn't something that falls over the world in an instant. True. But there comes a moment when, suddenly looking out at the street, one can say, "It's night already." This was said by the man eating peanuts, and we all went out onto the balcony to check.

On the way to the Costanera we said very little. We were crossing Azopardo when the man nearest to the sidewalk asked, "You think it's appeared already?"

And the woman next to the wall said, "Better if it has. Then when we get there we'll see it suddenly, over the river."

"The river?"

I don't know who said that. It didn't much matter. I realized that I too, since I'd read the announcement in the paper, had imagined it like that: with its tail of powdered stars extending down into the river. But there's no real river in Buenos Aires any longer.

"Grass and mosquitoes, that's all there is on the Costanera Sur," said the man on my right.

"Still, the place has kept its magic," (the woman behind). "It's as if it has preserved a memory of the river." I recalled the majestic ghost of the Municipal Balneario Beach, the square celebrating the triumphant arrival of the Solitary Seaman, Luis Viale and his stone lifebelt about to dive (into a muddy lot where there are now only screeching magpies) to save the victims of the shipwrecked Vapor de la Carrera. I recalled the drawbridge, the same bridge I'd crossed in the No. 14 streetcar when my mother took me to the Balneario, so familiar that I could tell the width of the beach by the height of the water hitting the stone wall. I loved that bridge, the breathless wait on the days when it opened leisurely to allow a cargo ship to pass, the suspense as it closed again, since the slightest mistake in the position of the tracks (I

suspected) would provoke a terrible derailment. And the joy when the
streetcar emerged unscathed and the river lay waiting for me. The river was
like life: the comet was something else. The comet was like one of those
moments of ecstasy that can only be found in books. Distractedly, I knew that
it would return one day, but I didn't expect it to. Because in the days when
happiness consisted in playing in the mud of the Balneario, any comet
or paradise glimpsed beyond my twentieth year didn't merit being
dreamed about.

"And here I am walking across that bridge," I said to myself, "not so
different from the person who once crossed it in a streetcar so as not to love it
still, nor so decrepit as not to be on the verge of shouting with joy, as I march
in procession to meet the comet with this bunch of lunatics.

It took me a while to realize that the word "procession" had occurred to
me because of the mass of people who, on foot or in cars or trucks or even in
a tractor, were gathering together in greater and greater numbers as we
approached the Costanera.

The Costanera itself was a virtual wall. Between the crowd trying to
find a good spot from which to view the sky, the smoke from the improvised
bread-and-sausage vendors, and the absence of spotlights, the only thing
visible from the Boulevard de los Italianos (where we now found ourselves)
was a bloated amoeba of more or less human consistency, into which we
were sucked and which didn't stop moving and humming.

"Over there, over there." Not far from me, a forceful voice managed to
emerge from the amoeba. Several of us turned to look. I detected a thin and
knotted index finger pointing toward the northeast.

"Where? I can't see a thing."

"There. Can't you see it? A fraction to the side of those two stars. About
this far away from the horizon."

"But is it rising?" asked an anguished voice to my left.

"Well, it's rising slowly."

I thought I saw it, gently separating itself from the tiny light of a booth or
something, close to the horizon, when behind me a hoarse voice shouted,
"No, it's there, far up. To the right of the Three Marys."

I had no trouble finding the Three Marys and I was scrutinizing their
right side when I heard a child's voice full of enthusiasm: "I see it! There it is!

It's huge!"

I looked for the child's finger and, somewhat hopefully, for something huge in the direction his finger indicated. In vain.

"You know what the problem is?" said a voice almost in my ear. "We're looking for it straight on. And that can't be done: it can't be seen straight on. What we should do is stand sideways and look for it out of the corner of our eyes."

I turned halfway round. I noticed that several other people had done the same, only they turned sideways relative to different things. I shrugged and looked upward out of the corner of my eye, first with my right eye and then with my left. A hand touched my ankle. Startled I looked down. There were several people lying on the ground.

"Can I give you some advice?" came a voice next to my feet. "Lie down on the grass. That way, face up, you can see the whole sky at once and I think you should be able to find it immediately."

Obediently I lay down next to several strangers and again I looked upward. In the unlit and moonless night, under the continuous music of the universe, I felt on the point of discovering something that might have allowed me, perhaps, to continue with my life with a certain degree of peace. Then, a few yards away from my head, someone spoke: "Don't you realize it's useless to look up from the ground? The trick is to make a reticule with your fingers. Didn't you read that this reticular effect increases the power of your vision? It's just like having a microscope."

The microscope man seemed unreliable to me, so I never got around to trying the reticular effect. Somewhat disheartened, I stood up. I looked around me. Pubescent youngsters, hunchbacks, women about to give birth, people suffering from high-blood pressure, idlers, and matrons were simultaneously and noisily pointing at the zenith, at the horizon, at the fountain of Lola Mora, at the planes taking off from the Municipal Airport, at certain falling stars, at fireworks, at the Milky Way or at the unexpected phantom ship of La Carrera. Cross-eyed, frowning, using the reticular effect, twitching their ears, jumping on one leg, swinging their pelvises, using telescopes, microscopes, periscopes, or kaleidoscopes, through engagement rings, straws, the eyes of needles, or water pipes, everyone was peering at the sky. Each person was searching, among the avalanche of stars (cold and beautiful since the awakening of the world, cold and beautiful when the last little glimmer from our planet is extinguished), each one was searching among those stars for a singular undefinable light. We never even realized that we were discovering death. And yet that is what it was: we had lost, once again, our last chance. One day, like a melon, like a snake, like a scarf of light, like everything round or with a tail or resplendent that we can create through our sheer desire to be happy, the golden-tailed comet would spin again through the space that had been our sky. But we, we who struggled and waited that night under the impassive stars, we on this bank and shoal would no longer disturb the soft evening mist to chase it.

Translated from the Spanish by Alberto Manguel

JOSÉ LEZAMA LIMA

MY WIFE MARÍA LUISA

On the sociable roof garden,
with your life in danger,
you are reading the Bible.
It was your whole house
which now stumbles in the smoke.
You are reading the Bible
where a leaf
surpasses water
and generations.
Reading, you tremble
as you remember dead
siblings, Psalm 23.
Your mother used to read it
to her son who will die.
The daughter reads it
to her mother at the hour
of God's peace.
You are the sister who left,
the mother who went to sleep
in a cloud outside the window.
These four, at my side,
wake me up each day
to invigorate the morning

and to begin the thread of images.
Slowly, with silent dignity,
breaking *the seat of the scornful.*
When you fluff the pillows
filled with angel feathers,
I remember from afar
and faultlessly repeat: *He maketh
me to lie down in green pastures.*
When death fumes at the front
door, at the momentary wall,
you bring the rod and the crook.
Hence I measure the new expanse,
one must walk there like a blind man.
With the crook I astound
the level of the unknown tide
and touch the sponge of half-sleep
to return to earth.
With you death was prior
and ephemeral, and life prevails
for his name's sake.

January & 1972

Translated from the Spanish by Roberto Tejada

Paradise

A PORTFOLIO

Rodney Graham, *Cedars, Stanley Park (1)*, 1991–93.

Sergio Vega, *Jungle Beard* (detail), 1995–96.

Amalia Mesa-Bains, *Cihuateotl*, 1997.

Mel Chin, *Degrees of Paradise (Monitor Room)*, 1991.

Gabriel Orozco, *La Palma (The Palm)*, 1993.

Nari Ward, *Happy Smilers: Duty-Free Shopping*, 1996.

Lovett/Codagnone, *Palm Beach Honeymooners*, 1996.

Daniela Rossell, *Viking Cruises*, 1995.

José Alejandro Restrepo, *Musa paradisíaca (Paradisiacal Muse)*, 1996.

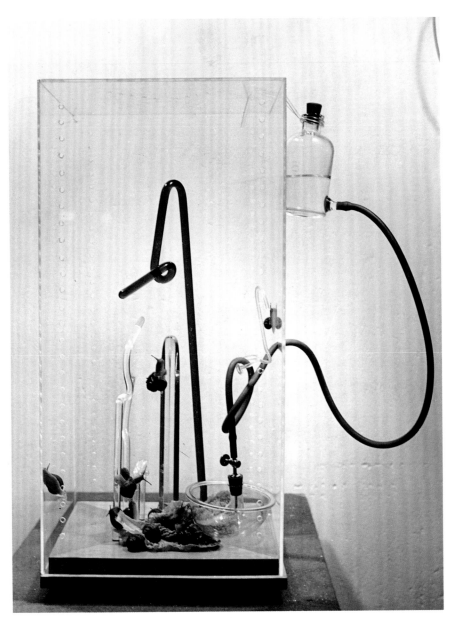

Luis F. Benedit, *Habitat para caracoles (Habitat for Snails)*, 1970.

Paradise

Paradise needs images. Words will not do; they articulate the distance between there and here. Dante's *Paradiso* is a visual program, as his great illustrators proved; Blake knew that the plates were crucial to the poems in his "illuminated books." The temporal nature of prose condemns it to failure, for Paradise must exist beyond time. On a tropical vacation, it is the photograph and postcard that matter most. Paradise needs to be remembered and invented at once.

It is a place to picture.

A collection of pictures can form a paradise. Museums were built on this model, ideally, redundantly, on islands or in parks. Habitats for experience outside of time. Museums came with a contradiction, as do all Edenic forms: the entry of outsiders augurs the end of the paradise. Now the best time to be in a big museum is when it is closed; favorite ones are both specialized and remote, like secret islands. Habitats for art: in the late eighteenth century, artists literally lived in the Louvre. Opening it to the public chased the natives out.

Inevitably Paradise becomes a place to order, even if only to realize one's vision of a so-called natural paradise. Disorder is Hell, while precision befits the godly. In the Paradise of exquisite detail that Beatrice offers Dante, nothing remains vague. Thus we cultivate our gardens; we curate our collections.

The idiom of Paradise has outlived our belief in it. Paradise provides a rich visual language to be entered, manipulated, and transformed. The transformations give life to the language. Its fertility is a measure of our desire.

ANN TEMKIN

LUIS RAFAEL SÁNCHEZ

For Rafi Rodríguez Abeillez

The whispering traveled from mouth to mouth. That Trinidad's son was tightening his cheeks until he suffocated his asshole. That he was a queer bird taking a vacation on land and sea. That he would don his Sunday best even when it was Monday or Tuesday. And that his vest was festooned with genuine-lace clovers. From loud and soft voices the hot, spicy, hateful comments came.

"Hum!"

At every turn, at every entrance, in closets, in doorways, in stores, in gambling dens.

"Hum!"

Every morning, at dawn, in the A.M., at noon, in the afternoon, in the evening, at night, and at midnight.

"Hum!"

The men, already sure of their game, would wait by the coconut grove to attack him with words.

"Fag!"

"Faggot!"

"Faggoty!"

"Drag queen!"

"Drooling drag queen!"

"Queer!"

"Sissy!"

The women let out volleys of laughter through their teeth and repeated teasingly:

"Madam!"

"Young lady!"

Until the feather-brained echo uncovered its voice by the river with an immense *hhh uuu mmm*. Trinidad's son, tired of being teased, locked himself in his miserable house to live out a lonely existence.

His dreams would alternate from girl to girl until the sun hit the countryside. Then, again the voices:

"He reeks of Com Tu Mi perfume!"

"He puts on eyeliner!"

"He's a party-going sissy!"

"Black men are very manly!"

"They aren't sissies!"

Ochoteco, who served him lunch, sent a note saying that she was sick and didn't want to cook for him anymore. Perdolesia brought him his ironed shirts and complained of rheumatism. She didn't take the dirty ones. Lulo the barber told him he wouldn't touch his "kink." And Eneas Cruz bought ductile wire to put up a fence to separate his house from that of Trinidad's son.

Trinidad's son stayed a long time with his head in limbo. Then he hid his face in his right shoulder. Like that, quietly, very quietly, he wept. Trinidad's son decided to leave town.

The whispering flew from mouth to mouth. That Trinidad's son was leaving because he despised dark-skinned men. That he was going to party with the whites because he was a good-for-nothing. And that he had gotten *skiiiiny* so he could be slender like a wasp. In every corner, the men would fling knives from their mouths:

"Trinidad's son is a bleached nigger."

"Trinidad's son is a good-for-nothing nigger!"

"Trinidad's son is a stiff nigger!"

The women, between one Amen and the next, took a minute to whisper.

"A bad example!"

"Gross!"

"Swine!"

"He's a pig!"

"He's two pigs!"

"He's three pigs!"

Trinidad's son wouldn't even bother to light his fire. From sunrise to sunset under the same roof. From sunrise to sunset like a body in a tomb. From sunrise to sunset like a cloistered nun. From sunrise to sunset tearing at scars. Until the day he left.

There was an abundant crop of gossip. That he would leave at night, so as not to say good-bye. That he would flee like a filthy Tom, Dick, or Harry. That he'd spit out memories of dark-skinned men. The men all stood around his house:

"You obscenity!"

"Pest!"

"Fool!"

"Spoiled brat!"

The women banged on coffee cans and ladled out the insults:

"Poison!"

"He's so squeamish!"

"Spineless creature!"

"He's so 'nice'!"

"Spoiled rotten!"

Trinidad's son waited until it was dark and left with a bundle in his hand: a linen suit, Vaseline, May Dreams powder, Come To Me perfume, a comb, and a ring. He hadn't gone three steps when a shadow fell on him and words were fired out:

"Smart aleck!"

Lifting his head he saw two thin shadows blocking his way.

"Faggot!"

"Swinger!"

Then, two *smart aleck*'s to the left and to the right two more *pompous nigger*'s. He stopped. *Pum, pum*, went his heart. In the night the shadows slipped away. In the corners, under the roofs, in the doorways. More, more, more shadows until no sight of light, the night without her nightly sounds and without stars, horrible, beardless night.

They pushed him. Fingers of one hand. He tasted dirt. The laughter roared as if the jaws of the region had been torn away. The murmuring was like a dart or a sword.

"Damn you to hell!"

"Don't come back!"

"Neither dead nor alive!"

The women were a screaming choir.

"Don't come back!"

"Don't come back!"

"Don't come back!"

He was able to get up. He looked both ways. The shadows multiplied like lizard eggs. From one, two, and from two, one hundred. It continued.

"Get the dogs!"

The voice was hoarse and exploded, pierced his ears. They waited for him. Mangy mutts, one-legged mutts, lame mutts, mutts with their barks muffled, in the back, in the legs. The pack pushed him down a path. It was a procession. The mutts and him. Behind them, the town. Or better yet, the town, then him, then the mutts and finally, always and again, the town. More blood, more pain, more laughter, more voices, more shadows, more black shadows of niggers, more black faces of niggers, more black tongues of niggers.

"Don't come back!"

"Don't come back!"

"Don't come back!"

Trinidad's son twisted like a hook.

"Don't come back!"

"Don't come back!"

"Don't come back!"

His arms stretched like a cross.

"Don't come back!"

"Don't come back!"

"Don't come back!"

The blood curdled through his skin.

"Party sissy!"

The opened wound in the blind night.

"Trinidad's son with his straightened kinky hair is nothing but a fag!"

He reached the river.

"Fag!"

"Fag!"

"Fag!"

The cold water and the hot blood.

"Pig!"

"Swine!"

"Pig!"

The filthy mutts stayed at the shore. Also shadows. And wounding voices.

"Partylovingfagpartylovingfagpartylovingfag!"

All the women. All the men.

"Don't come back!"

"Don't come back!"

The blood and the water pleased each other. Fewer voices, barkless, no, fewer shadows, return. The warm water, warmer, warmer. Voices, weaker and weaker. The water went plop. Then, *don't come back, don't come back, don't come back, son of Trinidad.*

gloop . . .

do

gloop . . .

not

gloop . . .

come back

gloop . . .

he

gloop . . .

sank.

Translated from the Spanish by Rose M. Sevillano

ARKANSAS

1. Cubie and Mt. Tabor

all the house is curved, all the sisters work at sonic, everybody talk like this:
I'm getting ready to tell you something; I know you ain't gon' like it: you remind me of a white man.
Where is your wife? I heard she was Anglo-Saxon. Bad as you used to talk about white folks.
Naw, for real, what is she? Eyetalian?
all the branches are curved green outside garden

Bukka neutral had a white woman in pine bluff
where it's past midnight for every every engine
but you know I'm so thankful Mr. Pascal
so thankful

like someone sanded the box of your voice
like a brass button

all the pink is gray some faded alpha bullshit and unpolished silver.
take a camcorder to this shit like some dynamite
blow that goddamn church up too
and let the hedge grow

2. Cash and Bryant

all the white folks mimi loves
have sunk into the moro bottom
they say to say hello
we just think she's precious

saline, pale ouchitah. panther.
fragments of airport, silent wine
Mississippi red table wine chilled
Temperance Hill and this pillhead

fucker named Steve uglyass
Miz Rogers cross-eyed cow
and that Elmer Fudd looking
principal. various Parkers and

Klappenbachs, Spearses, Matthews
and Gills

3. A Cricket

at midnight on reserve screen dim
bottom is dry and the guild of softwood
is sad. she know the cut is another rub
and the sound of that: whine and ring
scrawl. that same dark as before make
the window a background. the shelf
is full of animals. there's Jeffrey Wright.
and it ain't no turn no moose no buck
this mug has played on top of me
since Mama got that cake out the oven.
I was gon' say I know what art is; I know
how the world works: but the snows
came and my power is low. call Laura:
all you can do is go back to Arkansas.

THE

R O Y A L

FAMILY

WILLIAM T. VOLLMANN

I

Again he drove to Sacramento with its black parking lots given meaning by cars, its malls so thoroughly placed and identical in composition that every three or four miles one thought to be back at the same retail outlets no better or worse than the cigarette-burned pillowcases of San Francisco's whore hotels; and the night was hot and still. Dan Smooth sat out on his back porch on Q Street drinking rum.

Right on time, said Smooth, or at least I presume you're on time, because I can't see my watch. It's been a bad summer for gnats, I'm sorry to say.

Well, maybe the next one will be better.

Spoken like an optimist—hee, hee! And I'm just the opposite. I know I'm not your type, but you can't do without me, can you?

I'll hold judgment on that, Dan.

(Already Tyler was feeling the irritation. Smooth was fascinated by him and would not let him go, teased him and probed him, wanted to peer into him, but he did not want to share himself.)

And did you decide anything?

Yes, I did.

Well, tell me about it later. She moves around a bit, you see, Smooth explained. Hops around, like a lap dancer. You can't always say where she is, but you can *find* where she is, if you see the distinction.

Yeah, I get it, said Tyler, longing to look at his watch. He thought of the old criticism of Wagner: great moments and horrible half-hours. With Smooth the moments were horrible, too.

You plan to fuck her?

Well, your photo didn't really turn me on, Dan. No offense. I'm sure she's a nice Queen, though. I guess I'd just as soon keep it all business.

What does turn you on, Henry? queried Smooth, something moving in his face like the crawling silver shadows of change on a barmaid's chin as she counts it behind her half-wall.

As I said, I'd rather keep this professional.

Oh, get off your high horse! What are you afraid of? Don't you realize that you have the look in your eye of a man who has sexual relations with prostitutes, and don't you know that other men who do the same can always pick you out? You bear the mark of *Cain*, brother!

Tyler grimaced.

Have a shot, Henry?

All right.

There. Now what turns you on?

What turns *you* on, Dan? Child molesting?

I want to tell you something. I can tell a great deal about a man by his face. Not just his eyes, but his entire face. His mouth, for instance. I like to inspect a man's mouth. I can see from your mouth that you like to go down on women, Henry. I can see all their itty-bitty pubic hairs stuck between your teeth! (Oh, I could talk endlessly about textures. Maybe I don't have a moral sense, but that's normal. Maybe I do have one, but if so where did I put it?) I see I forgot to offer you a shot. Help yourself. Well, as I was saying, how do I know you don't suck guys? Well, because you never did come on to me, and I know I'm quite attractive. Elementary, as Sherlock used to say. You don't like me, do you, Henry? I can tell that from the color of your nose. You see, most other men, if they want something from me, they brownnose me a little. Why else do you think my asshole's so clean and shiny? They pretend not to mind—oh, they just have to pretend. Grin and bear it when I talk about what I talk about. But your nose is a good honest pink drinker's nose, and not a bit of shit on it. Now, as for your ears, Henry, I regret to tell you this, but you have *envious* ears. I'm not going to tell you how I know that, though, because old Dan Smooth's got to have a few secrets in this world, just to keep the ears of his fellow man envious. And, as for children, to answer your question, no, I can't tear myself away from them. If I were going to be marooned on a desert island and I could take only one food with me, you know what it would be? The earwax of a ten-year-old child.

What if it came out of envious ears? said Tyler.

Interesting case! But you still haven't answered my question.

All right, Dan. What turns me on is a sincere woman. That's all.

And what does she smell like?

You know, Dan, a lot of people on this earth fall in love with each other first and then have sex afterward.

But not you, Henry—ha, ha, not you! Remember, I can see your mark of Cain glowing right now in this darkness! It's brighter than my bug-zapper light! So don't lie to me, buddy, because we're both children of the same wicked God. Are you trying to deny that you care what they smell like?

That's right.

How about a high-grade armpit? Like roast coffee, almost—well, it depends on the—

Usually I shake hands instead of sniffing armpits, Dan.

Oh, then he likes mannish women. Office types, in executive blazers. But they use deodorant. Old Dan doesn't like that one bit. And you say it doesn't matter?

It's not my number-one concern.

So you'd do it with anyone then. You'd fuck anybody no matter how she smells. Talk about perversion. Talk about obscenity. This man dares to get sarcastic with me because I have certain fantasies regarding children, when he himself is nothing but a—I have no words—a mere functionary! There's something inconsistent about you—oh, yes, something *brutally untrue*. And you deny it; you deny your own animal nature. I disgust you, but what's inside your guts? Children of the same God, I said! And the Queen, she can see your mark of Cain! That's why she stayed away from you, because she's good. Whatever she does, she—oh, what's the use of explaining it to you? You don't see me as a human being; I'm just your way station. So. Where's my reward?

Right here, Dan. These Swedish postcards.

Well. *Well!* That was thoughtful. Are they illegal?

Probably. I didn't flash them at any cops—

Where did you get them?

From a friend.

How *nice* of him. *Or* her. Let me go inside and look at them. You wait here.

Give her this, said Smooth, returning a quarter-hour later. It's just glass, but she'll know what it is. Give it to some whore, and make up a good line, so the whore'll think it's something important, you see . . .

2

The sheets smelled of body odor. The closet door yawned and creaked. He turned on the television at once and kept it going loudly at all times, so no one would know whether he was there or not—better that they assume he was there, so they didn't break in. The door was barely held together by a pair of angle-nailed planks, and the bolt came out of the lock with a single tug.

He hadn't stayed at the Karma Hotel in a couple of years. He was ready to essay it again after his less than sleep-filled night at the Rama. The Karma had once been filled with the odors of fresh Indian cooking, but it didn't smell like curry anymore, and the old lady wasn't stirring her pot of beans, and her daughter no longer wore a sari, nor did she bear the round red caste-dot on her forehead. America the melting-pot! thought Tyler to himself. She looked much older, dirtier, and angrier.

Can I help you? she said, not recognizing him.

You have any rooms?

I.D., she said.

(That was new. They never used to ask for identification.)

He gave his driver's license and she wrote the number down, after which at her curt demand he surrendered twenty-five dollars, which used to be eighteen.

His room stank. On the television, a woman screamed.

It was almost sunset. Leaving the television jabbering away, he descended to Capp Street and found a girl.

My room? the girl said.

No, come up to mine, he said. I've got all the equipment there.

What, are you into S&M or something like that?

Something like that, he said.

Where you staying?

The Karma.

They don't let me in there.

Well, let's try.

What the hell, the girl sighed. Just as a tired barmaid draws her paper towel across the beer cooler in slow arcs, with untouched space in between, so Providence had incompletely abscessed this person, who still possessed many strangely healthy places on her thighs here bared to the open air.

What's yours, said Tyler, looking her over acutely, heroin?

Yup.

How many times a day?

Just five.

Well, that's not too bad, he said.

They went back to Mission Street where at the street grating he rang the buzzer, and someone let the lovebirds in, so they ascended the stairs to the second grating, which buzzed at their approach like the wing of an immense metallic insect, and then they were inside and facing the half-door behind which there had once been the smell of Indian cooking.

Can I help you? said the same woman.

Mutely, he showed her his key.

Don't get smart with me, the woman sneered. I was nice to you before but now I see what kind you are. You see this notice on the wall? **NO VISITORS.** You know what we call men like you? Trash collectors.

You gotta pay for my visit, idiot, the whore said.

He gave the woman a five, which she snatched with a snotty look. (He'd heard that the city planned to condemn this place.) Then she turned her back on them both, which he interpreted as permission granted for their private and consensual proceedings.

In his room the television was screaming again, because a murderer was eviscerating someone.

Pay me first, the girl said.

He gave her twenty.

Well, you gonna unzip or am I supposed to do that? she said.

You know the Queen, don't you? he said.

Oh, great, the girl said. Another fucking cop trying to jack me up.

From his night bag Tyler withdrew a fat manila envelope called
EVIDENCE.—This is from Dan Smooth, he said, breaking the seal.
Can you remember that name? And I'm Tyler.

Tyler, huh? How about if I just call you Blowhard?

I thought that was your job, said Tyler.

He upended the envelope over the bed, and a fat blue crystal fell
soundlessly out. —Now, this is one of the missing jewels to her crown, Tyler
explained. You wouldn't want to steal a jewel from your own Queen's crown,
now, would you?

The whore just stood there holding the twenty.

Now, am I a cop or not? he said.

You? You stink of cop.

All right. Fine. If I'm a cop, can I catch you any time or not?

Not if I run fast enough, sucker.

If I put the word out, you'll end up at 850 Bryant faster than you can put a
rubber on with your tongue.

I believe you, officer. You bastards always have all the power. But I'm no
rat. I'd rather be put away than rat on my Queen.

No one's asking you to be a rat, honey.

So what do you want? You want me to blow you and give you back the
twenty? God knows. I've had to do it before.

I want you to take this jewel to the Queen, he said. Then you can do what
she tells you to do. If you don't take this to the Queen, if you keep it for
yourself, then I'm going to have a problem with you, and once I tell the
Queen, she's going to have a problem with you, too. And tell her I'll be
waiting here.

That bitch downstairs isn't gonna let me in again. You gonna give me five
so I can—

That's possible. OK. So I'll be waiting on Capp and Sixteenth in two
hours, say, ten o'clock. If the Queen wants to give me any message or see me
herself, she can find me there. So here goes the jewel back in this envelope,
and there's a letter in there, too, in case you forget my name and Dan
Smooth's name, and, darling, here you are.

3

Queen or no Queen, it's getting old doing this, he thought—older if no

Queen. I'm getting old. Open the night case. Unlock the hard case and open that. That's not breaking the law, exactly, because a hotel room is a residence if you've paid for it, and even in California a citizen is allowed to play with his own possessions at home. The slide is open. Firmly thumb-nudge fifteen rounds into the magazine, which now waits ready to be fed into that oily hole, so do just that, then thumb the catch to close the slide: *snick*—a much less noisy sound than the bolt-slam of a street-sweeper shotgun, but authoritative nonetheless, and comforting to the prospective user. Now squeeze the release stud; catch the magazine as it returns to you, reborn from the grip. Fourteen rounds in it now; add one more copper candy (I recommend exploding hollow points). With the heel of your hand, shove the magazine back inside. Sixteen rounds, one of them chambered. Here it is now, your cold heavy little underarm pal. What would Smooth say about the smell of that? Zip up your jacket and look in the mirror to see how obvious the bulge is. If you feel so inclined, wash the lead off your fingers by means of this sink whose porcelain is stained yellow by the piss of whores and johns.

Increasing the volume on the television, which now offered for his moral furthering a science-fiction program about men kept as sex slaves in a world of beautiful hungry women, he went out, locked the door as far as it was capable of being locked, descended past the Indian woman, who cried out: Is she gone yet? If she isn't, you're gonna have to pay double. Is she still in your room? and after passing through both gratings, which is to say semi-permeable steel membranes, found himself gazing upon the red letters of the Walgreens pharmacy shining like stars, the tail of the "g" flickering. A rush of hatred for everything he saw spewed out of his soul, spreading like the concentric circular patterns of the subway station's tiles until it had reached the farthest building that he could see. Everything stank. A homeless man's fat dog ran past as quickly as a whore can stuff fifty bucks down between her tits. His owner, vainly seeking to overtake him, stumped along on crutches, a bedroll upon his shoulders, cursing. Right at the curb a quartet of mariachi musicians in white cowboy hats formed and began singing loudly, their blank faces and sadly drooping mustaches as red as new bricks in the rain. The red Walgreens sign made them redder. Now the night-leaners began to come out from their burrows, thickening the bases of lampposts while they got the lay of the land, then striding shadow-legged across the light-stained street. . . .

Five minutes before ten. He walked down Sixteenth past the old theater and waited. No whores at all, he saw; perhaps there's been a sweep; let's see, it was getting on the end of the month, so their general-assistance checks ought to have been long spent by now; where were they? A sweep, then; this was an election year.

Across the street an addict was mumbling, his words, like Dan Smooth's, reminiscent of the structure of graphite which is to say comprised of slender hexagonal plates of atoms which slough off at a touch like the multitudinous crusts of a Turkish pastry.

Then, at long last, the tall man came, tall as some dancer on stilts, that tall dark man who moved with easy intelligence, flaunting under his arm, his long gray arm which drooped down like a freeway off-ramp, the envelope called **EVIDENCE**.

Tyler raised his hand, like a parachutist about to pull his rip cord. —I'm the one, he said.

I'm not here to hurt you, the tall man said. She'll see you now.

You work for her?

You asking my business? said the tall man.

If you want to take me some place, I've got a right to ask what you do. I'm not messing with anybody's business. You can ask that chickie who brought you the envelope if I treated her wrong.

She went and told me you didn't pay for her time, the tall man said.

Well, I gave her twenty, Tyler said. You can either believe me or not believe me.

Matter of fact, I believe you. And I'm going to tell the Queen, too. That blond bitch can lie on her own time. Now, I don't have all night. You coming or not?

I'll walk with you, Tyler said.

The tall man slipped the envelope called **EVIDENCE** under the windshield of an abandoned car, and began to walk rapidly down Capp Street, never looking back. Tyler followed as quickly as he could. At Eighteenth they turned south and continued all the way to the old mayonnaise factory at Harrison without speaking, and then the tall man said over his shoulder: You a cop?

Nope.

You a vig?

What's that?

Vigilante.

Not me.

That's good. We don't have much use for vigs.

They kept walking, street to side street, side street to alley, and then suddenly they were in a tunnel that Tyler had never seen before, shiny-scaled like the Broadway tunnel upon whose walls crawled the ghosts of cars and the squiggly fire-lines of reflected taillights; but here there was no traffic, although from somewhere came the dull ocean-boom of many vehicles: no, it was stale air from many ducts, or maybe traffic from elsewhere coming through by conduction. The tunnel was narrow, and they went in single file, the tall man's heels ahead of him clapping lightly down upon plates of textured metal, the ceiling rainbowed with all the colors of dirty gold. Far ahead of them, he saw a shave-headed woman carrying a suitcase. She vanished into one of the square tomblike openings which had been so occasionally spaced into the yellow walls.

4

What about the octopus-minded of this world? They were wriggling their fingers, which were as thick and cold and white as the bars of a hospital bed. What about Tyler? Well, he was as confident (or unwary, perhaps) as the legs that march, run, trudge, and dance across that spidery whir of shade on the sidewalk where a maple's leaf-souls shimmered and shook in the shadow of a breeze; the legs were darkened and eaten by it as it trembled: what if the sidewalk opened suddenly there like a rotten decomposing glacier? Three policemen walked through the shadow, and their navy blue uniforms became darker. What if a world tore itself open right beneath their shiny shoes? Deep within, we might find people living according to the same cultural laws as that species of slavemaking ants called *Formica (Polyerges) rufescens*, about which Darwin wrote: *This ant is absolutely dependent on its slaves; without their aid, the species would certainly become extinct in a single year. The males and fertile females do no work of any kind, and the workers and sterile females, though most energetic and courageous in capturing slaves, do no other work. They are incapable of making their own nests, or of feeding their own larvae.* Down, down! A spider-girl's chin pressed itself against the floor, eyeballs rolling. Tyler experienced the same feeling that he always had when, after a long browse in the secret, cozy, and almost airy Poetry Room upstairs at City Lights where the window looked out on brick walls, a flat roof, and above everything a row of beautifully dancing laundry—he was almost in the sky, the world muffled and distant—he then passed the row of black-and-white beatnik postcards and began to descend the long steep black-treaded stairs which pulled him down past clumps of newspapers and manifestos, down, down, back into the world. *When the old nest is found inconvenient, and they have to migrate, it is the slaves that determine the migration, and actually carry their masters in their jaws. So utterly helpless are the masters that when Huber shut up thirty of them without a slave, but with plenty of the food they like best, and with their own larvae and pupae to stimulate them to work, they did nothing; they could not even feed themselves, and many perished of hunger. Huber then introduced a single slave (F. fusca), and she instantly set to work, fed and saved the survivors, made some cells, and tended to the larvae and put all to rights. What could be more extraordinary than these well-ascertained facts?*

What should I draw? said the Queen aloud. Something like a shark or a stingray. Nothing cute. My girls don't like nothing too cute. What's gonna make Domino happy? What's gonna make Strawberry come? What's gonna make Martha some fresh money? —Magic marker in hand, she upstretched against the concrete wall behind the grating, straining upward in her high heels so that her fringed skirt danced, smiling a little as she drew. She did the charcoal-colored eyes as far above her head as she could reach. The fringes quivered against her buttocks. Her little feet silently slid upon the light-pocked concrete.

A woman with two shadows raised and lowered her arm with a strangely mechanical air. Her ankle-length white dress was as porcelain. She froze, turned, seeming to stand on a rotating platform rather than move herself. Her hand-edges chopped air like knives. She bent, bowing to one of her shadows, while the shadow behind bowed to her. Now she joined with her shadow, becoming a vast writhing mound.

What is it, Sapphire? asked the Queen.

The porcelain woman covered her face and giggled. Then she began to stammer: S-s-s-some-b-b-body . . .

Oh, somebody's here, huh? What a good girl. Always looking out for your

Queen. C'mere, baby. Queen's gonna kiss your pussy . . .

L-l-l-uh . . .

Love you, too, Sapphire. Lemme kiss you. Quickly now. Can't keep guests waiting.

The girl approached, shyly scuttling sideways, timidly entered the Queen's arms. Sweat formed like milk on her porcelain face, and her pale legs began to writhe in the darkness.

Uh-uh-uh. Oh. Oh. *Oh*, oh, oh.

That's a good girl. That's my girl. You'll always be Queen's little girl. Now go let the man in.

5

An old, old face, he thought when he saw her: a face without any whites in the eyes anymore, a palish head upon a dark dress. Old, but maybe not so old —but a middle-aged black woman, just as Smooth had said. Older than in the photo—old, old!

What's your name, please, ma'am? he said.

Africa, replied the woman with a faint smile. I'm the Queen.

She had a codeine girl's sleepy froggy voice, her perfume and soft crackly sweater further manifestations of the same, a narcotic, blood that dizzied with a sweet scent that was half a stench.

Hunched and kneeling, with her hands over her face, the porcelain girl was a whitish thing, a strange staring thing, her dress like a sail catching in a breeze. It widened as she leaned back and spread her legs. Imperceptibly it stretched, like a sail catching air. Her eyes almost closed, her wrists gripped one another in turn. Then she began to masturbate. In the stillness, Tyler could hear the creaking of her shoes. She began to club her temples with her bent wrists, like a wrought-up wind-up doll.

Take my cigarette, said the Queen to Sapphire. And go make them be quiet.

The porcelain girl fled, her shining mouth pulsating with strings of mucus. Distant whispers ceased, and the silence crawled in his ears like sweat.

Are you the one who wrote me that letter? said the Queen.

Yes, ma'am.

What kind of work do you do?

I'm a P.I.

You're carryin' a piece, the Queen said.

Yes, ma'am.

Justin, take his piece.

Tyler hesitated for a moment. Then, deciding to see matters through, he drew the gun out, careful to keep it downpointed.

Mind if I make it safe? he asked.

Go ahead.

He dropped the magazine out, brought the slide back to unchamber the sixteenth round, put magazine and cartridge into his coat pocket, handed the tall man his gun.

And you're Tyler? said the Queen.

Yes, ma'am.

He heard a sharp click and tensed, believing for a moment that somebody had loaded his gun, but then the omniscient flashlight showed him a drop of water trembling on the concrete ceiling; when it fell to the floor, its echo harshly slammed. He nodded then. The Queen's eyes glittered ironically.

And why are you here? she said then.

I—I want to know you, he replied, to his own surprise.

Ah, said the Queen.

He waited.

Down on your belly, said the Queen. Hands behind your head.

He obeyed. He was in for anything now. The floor was damp.

Okay. C'mere. Stay on your belly. Crawl over here like a worm. Closer. Now slide your hands down the back of your neck. Raise your head and look at me. Can you see me? Now I'm going to spit in your mouth. I want you to raise your head and open your mouth wide for me like a little baby bird.

She leaned forward, her eyes hurting and confusing him, and her face descended, her eyes shining almost malignantly, and then her full lips began to open and somebody shone the flashlight on them and her lower lip began to glisten with spittle, and then a long slender thread of it crawled down from her lip, with much the same speed as a spider descending its strand, and he was shocked to find how much he wanted that spittle inside his mouth. He didn't even know why he wanted it. Warm and thick, it began to coil round and round upon his tongue. He felt it before he tasted it. She leaned closer, her face above him like a falling planet so that she was almost kissing him. Then a foaming frothing tide of saliva spilled into his mouth as she breathed on his face. Her breath smelled like cunt. Her spit tasted like cunt.

Later, when she let him go out, he saw the spider-girl advancing on her chin, on her knees and on her palms.

6

He went home and added to the details description sheet:

```
TEETH          White
EARS           Oval, L ear only pierced
FINGERNAILS    Long, unpainted, dirt under nails
```

He went back to the beginning of the form, thought for a while, and wrote:

```
AGE            Approx. 45
```

Then he changed it back to:

```
AGE            Approx. 40
```

He made other corrections:

```
CLOTHING       Castoffs? Sweatshirt, jeans, tennis shoes
JEWELRY        Large hoop earring in L ear, bangles on left wrist
PECULIARITIES  Round scar on right calf (bullet wound?),
               abscess marks on arms, tattoo of skull on left
               wrist, mole on left cheek, strong smell of
               perfume
```

He stared at the form, which now seemed as vain to him as the scribbles on the walls of a residential hotel. He felt tired and woolly-headed. There was, as Smooth had said, absolutely no reason for him to be seeking out the Queen. But the seeking was over now, and maybe something would come next, something, no doubt, which would rouse either further sadness or further alarm. It was his characteristic to admit to what he could not change, to himself if not to others.

On the details description form he added to PECULIARITIES: Lesbian or bisexual.

7

Now, the court thing, I have absolutely no control there, Dan Smooth was saying on the phone. And I don't have the time to get involved.

He hung up. —FBI turds, he muttered.

Lacing his fingers together, Dan Smooth surveyed Tyler and said: How did it go?

I saw her, said Tyler. I don't know what to make of it.

I like you more and more, Henry. You don't bullshit. Sit back, relax, pour yourself some Black Velvet. Working-man's drunk. I want to finish watching this. I was right in the middle of the good part when that administrative bitch called. Speaking of bitches, how's Mugsy?

How do you know the name of my mother's dog?

It's in your file, fella.

You've been spying on me?

For the Queen, agreed Smooth. He turned the knob of the dusty old television set which was not quite at arm's length from his eyes and indented the blue button of the videocassette recorder. The movie resumed.

The girl shook her hair out of her eyes as the man put his penis into her butt. There was not any sound.

Imagine videoing this, said Smooth. Imagine the *happiness*.

Tyler sighed and poured himself a drink. —Yeah, just imagine, he said.

Let me find this, muttered Smooth. Just one second. Now, see, what I'd really like to find here . . .

A young boy's milk-white buttocks were wiggling.

There was one other kind of really really bizarre scenario, said Smooth. It involved lots and lots of toilet paper. No, you really have to see this.

Here were glowing aliens, shimmering green watercolor light; the aliens kept bowing toward each others' middles.

To me this is really erotic, said Smooth. Really really erotic. Almost always, part of it is the fantasy aspect. Now, in this one, I'm the father and he's the bad boy. I'm saying right here: Are you ready for a B.M. fantasy? and he says yes. I say, lean back in this chair. He says, Danny, I've had this fantasy, too.

You think he meant it or was he saying it to get more money out of you?

I think he meant it, Henry. I wasn't paying him anything.

Tyler refilled his glass.

He's already fourteen, Smooth went on. I still love him. These things happen. Also, as I was telling you earlier, the whole thing happened in my mind.

You mean he's just virtual?

Well, it's a confessional time for me, said Smooth almost shyly. I also really don't want to like fuck up and do something evil. This scenario is . . .

His voice became silent for a moment. Then he said: I never hurt anybody, Henry.

I believe you, Tyler said. I guess I'm a Canaanite, just like you said.

The Queen saw that right off, Henry. Don't think she didn't. You're in now, boy.

Smooth swallowed, drummed his fingers, and gazed into Tyler's face very very earnestly. Finally he whispered: See, there is this other thing. The Queen is so gorgeous sometimes. And always so special to me.

8

Down the hall from the room upon whose door a sign read DO NOT DISTURB — I DON'T HAVE NOT A THING —PLEASE DO NOT KNOCK, there was a room on whose door somebody had written and taped a sign which read IF YOU WANT SOMETHING, DON'T ASK. IF YOU REALLY NEED IT, GO ELSEWHERE, and across from that door was a door charred and kicked and smeared and scraped, whose upper half had been replaced by plywood already splintered by abuse, and whose doorknob had given way to a handle held in place by two Phillips-head screws now worked half out; Tyler had had to turn them in again with the point of his pocketknife; and inside that room, rendered holy by an incandescent doughnut in place of any lightbulb, Dan Smooth was sitting at the foot of the bed like a wise grave doctor; and the junked-out whore named Sunflower, who'd a quarter-hour before stirred the white lump into the rust-colored liquid in the bottle cap, heated it to bare lukewarmness, and fed it to her hungry arm on the second stab, now lay on her side mumbling so sadly in a soft hoarse voice; she was naked because Tyler had given her money for the dope, and so when she came with him she'd stripped by habit; it was likewise by habit as well as concern that Tyler sat stroking her pimpled buttock as he would have stroked the forehead of a good dog or a sick child.

'Cause I slept there all night, he bought me a burrito and then he told me: That's four dollars right there. That's how he treated me, the whore said. Are you listening to me?

Yeah, I'm listening, sweetheart, said Tyler.

Sighing, Dan Smooth got up and began to piss gently into the sink. When he had finished, he stood there for a moment buttoning his fly. Then he lightly tapped his fingernail against the tap.

The whore's eyes jerked open in terror. —Is that a knife? she said.

It's okay, Tyler said.

What is it? Is it a gun? Is he loading a gun?

No, honey. He's just making music in the sink.

Oh, said the whore, subsiding. He heard her weary breathing. He liked her and was sorry for her. She was twenty years old and looked fifty. She was ruined.

I have so much respect for you and the both of you that I trespass with, she said with an effort.

I respect you, too, Sunflower, he said.

Hey, can you pop this zit on my butt?

This one? It's pretty flat.

I want the white stuff to come out, the whore fretted. Can you pop it for me, please?

Okay, said Tyler, setting thumb and forefinger like pliers about the red spot and digging into the flabby flesh. Nothing came out.

Is that better? he said.

Yeah, that's a lot better, she sighed. Feels like a lot of white stuff came out. You wanna know me? You wanna listen to me? Are you listening to me?

Here I am, Sunflower. Here I am listening.

My father fucked my sister first time when she was five. He fucked her doggy-style, and he put his hand over her mouth so she couldn't scream. Her pussy was all bloody and her asshole was all bloody. There was blood coming down to her knees. Then he fucked me when I was five, and then he fucked my other sister when she was five. My other sister went and told on him. So me and my sister told my father not to do that no more . . .

And he listened to you?

Yeah, the whore said. Tears boiled out of her eyes.

He stopped fucking your little sister? said Tyler gently.

Yeah. He, uh, well, he . . . he . . .

He fucked you and your older sister instead?

Just me, she sobbed. My sister couldn't take it. Said it hurt too much. But I
—I heard the youngest crying, and when I saw the blood, I knew . . .

It's okay now, sweetheart. It's okay.

I wanna be a shield, she said. I was a shield for my sister, and now I protect
all the men who come to me. They give me their pain. It comes out their
cockheads. It just hits me. It just hurts me. It stays with me. That's all I
wanna do. I wanna be a shield for all the men in this world, and all the
women, and all the kids. They can come and shit on my face if they want to;
they can even shit on my goddamned face. You wanna shit on my face?

No, thanks, said Tyler, squeezing her hand. That wouldn't make me feel
happy.

But did she spit in your mouth?

Yes, she did.

I knew it. I could see it.

She lay still for a while. Dan Smooth opened the tap but no water came
out.

Hey, how much did you gimme? she said.

Twenty.

And what about your friend? Why's he listening? He was supposed to
gimme thirty, and he didn't give me squat.

He'll give you ten.

I love you, the whore wept. I love you. I'm so alone and I have so many
contacts.

I love you, too, said Tyler, because he would have been her shield, too, if he
could.

No! she screamed. Don't say that! I'm here and you're not here—

She fell asleep, and began snoring loudly. Mouth open, face flushed, she
opened and then reclosed her eyes, sinking into the earth of dreams, her
knees studded with immense white circular scars, her black-grimed toes
faintly twitching, and in her sleep she continued to scratch at those angry
speckles on her buttocks.

Four knocks, and they let the Queen in. The Queen was alone, but three tall black men stood waiting in the hall outside. She was wearing a man's hooded sweatshirt which shadowed and overhung her dark old face into anonymity. Dan Smooth bolted the door. She put her left arm on her hip, threw her head back, and extended her right wrist to be kissed. Tyler got down on his knees to do the honors. —You brownnoser! laughed the Queen, pleased. Now what about you, Danny boy?

Dan Smooth bent over the Queen's hand.

The Queen shook her hood off and stood there for a moment, smiling almost grimly. On the bed continued the long, slow, gasping breaths of sleep.

You gentlemen owe me twenty in visitor fees, she said.

This dump charged you?

They always charge me. They don't know.

One Queen, three bodyguards, cackled Smooth, pulling a twenty-dollar bill from his sleeve.

Good arithmetic, said the Queen. But why can't you multiply?

They're not old enough to bleed when I fuck 'em, said Smooth.

Did you get off on Sunflower's story? said Tyler challengingly. She bleeds from both ends.

You don't need to pick on him, Hank, said the Queen. Danny's a good man. Sunflower's daddy wasn't. We would have taken care of him but Sunflower didn't want that. Sunflower's my baby, she cooed, kissing the woman's dirty toes.

She turned to Tyler and said: You see what she's about? You see why she's good? Jesus Himself ain't fit to pop her zit like you done. Jesus on the very cross of torture and shame never suffered like she suffered. And I don't care how much He gave. He never gave like she did. I know her so well. Queen's come to give her little baby her reward. My baby, my darling little baby. Queen's heart is gonna break.

And between the naked woman's legs she laid five hundred dollar bills and a baggie with enough China White for Sunflower to kill herself ten times over.

Tyler said nothing. The Queen looked him in the eye and said: It's up to her. Gotta give her some happiness. If she don't OD, she can come back to me for more favors. Queen'll always take care of her. If she wants to go into rehab she can. If she wants to sell that powder she can. But I know she gonna wanna take that happiness. I know she gonna wanna go home.

9

He saw that for himself, said Smooth, and Tyler realized now that the Queen, who was both very busy and very subtle, had come not only to see to Sunflower but also to judge him and perhaps try him more deeply also. Spitting in his mouth wasn't enough. —I can vouch for old Hanky-Panky here, Smooth went on. He saw the goodness. We don't none of us have to be riding with him. I knew his sad eyes from the first. He and Sunflower have the same sad eyes.

How many are like her? said Tyler.

She's one of the best right now, the Queen said. Queen's not gonna tell you all she knows, but there's several. Well, they wear out. In this town, maybe twenty thirty forty girls are our shields. Take the pain and keep it. They help all the rest. You wanna see how much pain she's got inside her? Look here.

Partly unzipping her sweatshirt, she reached down her neck and presently pulled out what resembled a copper penny with eyes and lightning bolts carved or engraved into it, and protruding octopus-fashion from its edges many copper wires knotted into tiny holes in the disk; the ends of the wires had been wrapped around what might have been black seeds.

Got any rubbers on you, Smooth? she said.

Let's see now. Let's see, the man said, thoughtfully licking his lips. Oh, here's an old dried-out one under the bed. Smells pretty fresh . . .

Well, whack it against the wall or something. Clean it off.

How about a plain rubber band? said Smooth. I keep one around my address book.

Yeah, that'll do. Now tie it around the charm, *respectful* like. Good. You just watch this, Hank. Don't say nothing; don't do nothing. Just *observe*. Danny, hold the rubber part. Don't touch the copper, 'cause it's magic. Now touch it to her. Slowly. No, wait. You do it, Smooth. But she's used to you, Hank, so you should hold her hand. She's gonna be scared. Okay, Danny boy. Give him a show. It's only a show.

Dangling the copper spider by its improvised thong, old Dan Smooth, holding his breath, bent over the recumbent woman and slowly began easing it down above her ankle while the Queen stood praying: *In the name of the Mother and the Daughter and the Holy Ghost!* and the strands of wire began to writhe and quiver of their own accord. One touched flesh, and the light flickered and went out, and the stinking darkness exploded with deep blue sparks and Sunflower jerked up screaming like she had that first time when her father sodomized her and in the room across the hall a radio immediately went on loud because they didn't want to know about any screams. Tyler felt no electric shock. He held Sunflower's hand as tightly as he could and wiped the tears from her eyes, and then the lights came back on as Dan Smooth took the talisman away and Sunflower fell back on the bed snoring.

She won't remember nothing, said the Queen. See, that's all the pain she has inside her. Too much for any human being to get out even by magic.

10

We take pride in our Queen, because she has the power, Smooth was explaining brightly. Glowing in the darkness. Talk about animal magnetism! Well, believe you me . . .

It didn't hurt her, Hank, if that's what you're thinking, said the Queen.

What about *his* pain? asked Smooth, with a sickening mixture of malice and pity. Henry'd be a crybaby if he knew how—look into those eyes of his, Maj; how can we get that pain out of his eyes?

That's what everybody asks me, said the Queen with brightly bitter humor. —As if I'm not the biggest shield of them all. Well, it's an honor, I know.

Tyler said nothing. —Of course it's only his second time, Smooth finally blurted, looking him up and down shaking his head.

(Outside, in the hallway, an old woman was shouting: Fook-a you, beetch! Goddamn it! Fook-a you! Oh, I sorry. I fook-a you today, you fook-a me tomorrow. Fook-a I sorry!)

Smooth leaned forward and whispered so that the hot wet breath tickled Tyler's ear: Now imagine if Sunflower woke up and *we* knew but *she* didn't know that there was a window there.

PAINTING SHUTTERS

A woman unloading
Her station wagon

Bobbed hair, a white blouse
I'm not sure

I saw her face
Even her hands

But her skirt
Was tight and black

She moved
Like someone I knew once

In that stalling air.
Waiting every day

Fixing martinis,
Sweeping the floor

Sitting in front of the door
Where palms skipped about

On the boulevard. Such traffic,
All those voices in Spanish

JAMES WELLING

RAILROAD
TOWNS

Road Near Morgantown, WV; 1993.

Century House, Grafton, WV; 1993.

Pittsburgh, PA; 1991.

Cohoes Falls, NY; 1994.

Telephone Poles, Selkirk, NY; 1994.

Palmer, MA; 1992.

Dark House, Brownsville, PA; 1993.

JAMES WELLING

James Welling's photographs focus on a specific geographical site: the Northeast Corridor of the United States, where he grew up—near Hartford, Connecticut—and where he began his schooling. But he is interested in more than making handsome images of characteristic architecture, regional landscapes, or the evanescent particularities of light and shadow. Issues of memory, history, and culture are subtly but insistently layered in his images in ways that can only be discerned and unraveled through thoughtful contemplation.

In the images reproduced here, Welling seems to use some of the same motifs that Walker Evans claimed as his own over sixty years ago: American vernacular architecture and the melancholy towns it inhabits were Evans's most poignant subjects. But for Welling they speak more about the continuing grip of the past than about the cultural poverty of the present. Unlike Evans, Welling doesn't look for the metaphoric grave marker towering over an industrial town's grimy streets or the deadening regimentation of company-owned housing. Instead, he fashions an oblique view of the average and the commonplace. Guided by the artist's sidelong glance, the viewer seems to come upon the simple geometries of houses, say, in Grafton, West Virginia, as if just passing by. Welling's images remain a mystery—a brush with the uncanny that reaches back to childhood, when the elusiveness of the meaning of many things engendered a mixture of fantasy and fear.

It is significant that one of Welling's primary subjects is the domestic dwelling, where the child's imagination roams in anticipation— who lives there? is that old lady really a witch? —and where adult realizations settle in resignation. Although Welling gathers connotations from a wide field of knowledge, including the history of photography and the culture of the constructed American town, his images can be best understood by the imagination.

CAROL SQUIERS

JOÃO CABRAL DE MELO NETO

WINDOWS

There's a man dreaming
on a beach, another
who never remembers dates.
There's a man running away
from a tree, another missing
his boat or his hat.
There's a man who's a soldier,
another who's an airplane,
another who keeps forgetting
his time his mystery
his fear of the word veil.
And there's yet another who,
like a ship, has fallen asleep.

WATER AND THE POEM

The poem's liquid voices
invite me to crime
a revolver.

They tell me of islands
not even dreams
can reach.

With open book on my knees
and wind in my hair
I gaze at the sea.

What happens in water
is repeated
in memory.

Here the sea is a mountain
fair and blue and round,
taller than the coral reefs
and shallow swamps to the south.

From the sea you can extract
(from the sea that laps our coast)
a thread of precise light,
metal or mathematics.

In the city itself
old lanky row houses
rub their chalky shoulders
on either side of a river.

From these houses you can learn
a lesson of long experience:
a delicate equilibrium
in writing, as in the architecture.

And from this indigent river,
this blood-mud that meanders
between cement and sclerosis
with its torpid march,

and from a people who stagnate
in the river's mucous membranes,
entire lives rotting
—one by one—to death,

you can learn that man
is always the best measure,
and that the measure of man
is not death but life.

TOURIST PITCH FOR RECIFE

CEMETERY IN PARAÍBA (BETWEEN FLORES AND PRINCESA)

This cemetery is a house
for those who herein lie.
A house without attachments,
a house of just one story.

And of this house, just the part
within the stucco walls.
No one ever used the garden,
much less the surrounding yard.

Too small to be a hotel,
it's more a boardinghouse,
with a cemetery lobby
just big enough to hold

those few residents who,
coming here, refused
the privilege of city cemeteries
in cemetery cities.

THE SEA AND THE CANE FIELD

What the sea learns from the cane field:
the horizontal style of its verse;
the georgics of street poets, uninterrupted,
called out in parallel chant and silence.
What the sea doesn't learn from the cane field:
the passion of a rising tide;
the thresh-hand of waves on the sand,
ground by the pounding into powder.

⋆

What the cane field learns from the sea:
the quiet rhythm of advancing waves;
the meticulous spreading of water on land,
filling every hollow, wherever it passes.
What the cane field doesn't learn from the sea:
the intemperance of the cane's outpouring;
the moderation of the plantation-sea
which pours forth with less brutality.

FORT ORANGE, ITAMARACÁ

The rough stone of war,
its rugged, granitic grain,
was besieged and overrun
by moss and mistletoe.
Next to the stone which time
erodes, beating like a pulse,
the uneroded canon metal
seems eternal, absolute.
But the punctual trickling
of time penetrates all;
even if not felt, its pulse
continues its pointed beating,
and the vegetal guerrillas
can count on time's trickle
in their silent infiltration
against the widowed iron.
And one day the hard fingers,
the canons' vain rigidity,
will also surrender to time
and its rhetoric, its regularity;
trickling, unheard and unchecked,
it will force them to embrace,
penetrate and possess
one another, iron and moss.

THE SCHOOL OF KNIVES

On reaching the northeast the trade wind
sweeps through coconut and cane fields;
coursing their leaves it whets itself
on the blades, scaling knives, cleavers.

Once it has flown past the fertile Mata
its hands, which were round and female,
acquire the appetite and teeth of knives,
with which it traverses other regions.

The coconut tree and cane stalk teach it,
not with the grindstone but knife to knife,
how to fly through the Sertão backlands,
sharp hand drawn and ready to strike.

PLANTATION BOY

The cut sugar stalk is a sickle.
Cut at a sharp angle it gains
the whetted edge of the sickle
that cut it to a sickle: a mutual giving.

When I was a boy, the edge of a stalk
once cut and almost blinded me,
and a scar which I do not bear
knew how to bear itself in me.

I no longer have the scar,
but the germ is in me still;
I have never discovered if
it's a virus or a vaccine.

Translated from the Portuguese by Richard Zenith

THOSE
LOPES

An evil breed who give you no peace: I want to stay a thousand miles away
from them. Even from my sons, all three. A free woman, I don't feel old or
defeated. With age comes quality. I love a man, and my skills make him
marvel, his mouth water. My desire now is to be happy, day to day, whether
suffering or celebrating. I want to speak clearly. Let no Lopes come near,
or I'll chase him off with my teeth bared. What's behind me, all I went
through, has vanished and been forgotten. At last I've found the essence of
my heart. The greatest gift is to be a virgin.

But first others write our story.

As a little girl, I saw myself dressed in flowers. But what stands out earliest
is the poverty. What good were a mother and father if I was orphaned by
money? I became a young woman without letting my innocence destroy me: I
sang children's tunes mixed with romantic melodies. I wanted to be called
Maria Miss, hating the name I was given: Flausina.

God gave me this black beauty mark on the whiteness of my chin—I
looked pretty even when I saw my face reflected in the swill in the pigs'
trough. And he passed by, a Lopes, wearing a big hat with the brim turned
down. They're all good-for-nothing, but this one, Zé Lopes, was the worst,
an arrogant seducer. He looked at me, and I stood there, trembling
helplessly, nailed by his gaze.

He passed on horseback, in front of the house, and my father and mother
greeted him, sullen as they never were with others. Those Lopes and their

breed came from another riverbank. They bought or seized everything, and if it weren't for God they'd be masters here to this day. People should be meek, mild, like flower blossoms. Mother and Father didn't lift a finger to defend me.

Little by little I remember. . . .

With barely enough time to weep, I wanted at least a trousseau, like other girls, the illusion of an engagement. What did I get? Neither courtship nor church. With his hot hands and short arms, the man grabbed me and took me to his house, to his bed. But I learned to use my better judgment. I stifled my tears. I endured that body.

I did what he wanted: I talked dirty. The devil makes some men want exactly that: fabrication. Those Lopes! With them if there's no hay, there's no milk. When he gave me money, I acted nice. I said, "I was a two-bit virgin, now I've got three bits." He liked that; he didn't know I was watching and waiting.

He put a scrawny black woman in the house to keep an eye on me. Miz'Ana. Whom I learned to deceive, finagling accounts, and whom I called godmother and friend. I managed to make life smooth on the outside. It was lying on my back that I felt the world's sordidness, the devil's nightshirts.

No one has any idea what it's like: all night scrunched up on a cot, with the clumsy, dull weight of the other hemming you in, the stink, the snoring— these and so many other abuses. I, a delicate girl, held captive, with him always there, smothering me in the dark. It's harmful, a man hatching his hidden thoughts, as one day devours another—how do I know what perversities he snored? All of this tarnishes a bride's purity, infects like a disease, pierces the spirit. As sure as I'm here today, in a way I never was before. In such a small space, I was squeezed smaller, and on the wall my fingernail scratched out prayers and my longing for other horizons.

I traced the alphabet. Needed to learn how to read and write. In secret, of course. I began from the beginning, aided by the newspapers used to wrap groceries and by the kids from school.

And the money came in.

As much as I could, I managed all that he had to my own profit. I scrimped. Had titles put in my name. Oblivious, he was making me richer. And once I gave birth to his son, his trust in me was total, almost. He got rid of Miz'Ana when I trumped up false charges: that that madam had goaded me to have carnal relations with another man, a Lopes too—who soon vanished from life, no one knows how.

Like they say: he who hears only half understands double.

I became a snake in the grass. In his liquor I put seeds, just a few, from the black calabash tree; in his coffee, liana bark and belladonna. Merely to cool down his rabid desire—I confess to no crime. Liana bark makes a man gentler, more refined. He was already looking yellowish, like an egg just laid by an ostrich. With little effort he died. My life was quite lethal. After the funeral I swept the house and tossed out the dust.

And did those Lopes leave me in peace?

Two of them, tough types, demanded my hand—the cousin and brother of the departed. I maneuvered in vain to keep the brutes at bay. One of them, Nicão, set a date: "Wait for me at the end of the requiem mass." Which would be in thirty days' time. But the other one, Sertório, lord and master, with gold and dagger in hand, didn't even wait seven days before barging into my house to claim me. I suffered admirably. How did I lead my life? Year after year of submissive subjection, as tiresome as catching rain in a gourd or chopping kale very fine.

Both men raging, oozing with jealousy. And for good reason—I set it up. Nicão kept circling the house. Were the two sons I bore really Sertório's? In any case, whatever he had, I made him pay for, quickly adding it to my account—honor included. I acquired new graces—and enjoyed them in the garden of myself, all alone. I assumed a more maidenly air.

Smiling, I leaned out the window, lips puckered: negotiable, impartial. Until my idea hardened into action. I knew he was a Lopes: unruly, fiery, foaming at the mouth. I saw him leave the house, in a rage, clothed in fury, his pockets full of slander. I'd sent the other one messages, coated with sugar. Lately I'd giggled for a reason. Good guy against good guy, my lightning bolts faced off amid shots and flashing steel. Nicão died without delay. Sertório lasted a few days. I wept, brokenhearted, according to custom, pitied by all: unfortunate woman, two almost three times a widow. On the edge of my property.

But there was still one left. Sorocabano Lopes: the oldest one, loaded with land. He saw me and got me into his head. I accepted with good grace; he was greedy for consolation. I stipulated: "From now on, only with a ring on my finger!" So great was his fervor that he agreed—which, for a man of his declining years, is like buttoning a button in the wrong hole. And that Lopes I treated very well and much better, fulfilling his desire.

I racked half my brain: I gave him rich, spicy meals and endless hours of pleasure—the guy was sapped dry from so much love and affection. All good things are good and bad for us. The one who died, at any rate, was him. And I inherited all he had, without the slightest qualm.

So finally, in the end, at last avenged. That vile breed is finished. As for my sons, all of them equally Lopes, I endowed them with money so they could drive their cattle far away from here. I'm done with quarreling: I've found love. I don't heed those who don't approve. I love, truly. I'm old enough to be his mother? Save your breath. I have no respect for calendars and dates.

I don't intend to give him free rein over my body. But I'd like, for my own sake, to have some children of another stripe, civilized and modern. I want the good life I never had. I want sensitive people. What use are money and understanding to me, if I can't settle with my memories? I, one day, was a very little girl. . . . We all live to serve some purpose. Enough of those Lopes! They make me sick.

Translated from the Portuguese by Richard Zenith

CARLOS DRUMMOND DE ANDRADE

A WOMAN WALKING NAKED THROUGH THE HOUSE

A woman walking naked through the house
envelops you in a tremendous peace.
No dated nakedness to arouse you here.
It's a walking dressed in nakedness,
a sister's innocence, a glass of water's.

The body gets no notice here,
only the rhythm that carries it along.
Curves pass in a state of purity
and give a name to life: chastity.

Hairs that once brought fascination don't arouse.
Breasts and buttocks (a tacit armistice)
at rest from war. I, too, at rest.

IN YOUR CRINKLY GARDEN BROWN ANEMONES

In your crinkly garden brown anemones
detain my anxious hand: Slowly.
Let each petal or sepal be caressed
unhurriedly, heaven; and let eyes alight,
an abstract kiss, before the kiss of ritual;
on the pubescent flower, love; and all is holy.

IT WAS A MORNING IN SEPTEMBER

It was a morning in September
and
she was kissing my member

Planes and clouds were passing
black choruses were roaring
she was kissing my member

My childhood time
my future time to come
were blooming now as one

She was kissing my member

A little bird was singing
deep within the tree, within
the earth and me and death

Death and springtime in the foliage
fought for the clearer water
water that redoubled thirst

She was kissing my member

Everything that I had been
everything forbidden me
held no meaning now

Only the curled-up rose
that burning stalk, a flame
that ecstasy upon the grass

She with kisses on my member

It was the most chaste of kisses
with unclothed purity
that belongs to given things

And it wasn't the homage of a slave girl
kneeling in the shadows
but the offering of a queen

becoming something of mine
circulating in my blood
soft and slow and wandering

the way a saint had kissed
in her most sacred rapture
and with a solemn shiver

kissing kissing my member

Thinking about all other men
I pitied them
imprisoned in the world

My empire extended out
across the whole deserted beach
alert to every meaning

She was kissing my member

The indictment of being
the mystery of existing
the incongruency of loving

were all silent waves
that died upon a distant dock
and a city rose up

radiant with precious stones
assuaging hate
and rapture came along upon the breeze

to steal me off
if first I hadn't stripped my leaves
the way a head of hair is smoothed

and I was all scattered
in concentric circles
in the haze of the universe

She kissed my member
                              kissed
and died while kissing
reborn in September

Translated from the Portuguese by Gregory Rabassa

THE TURTLE'S CRY

A Tale Told to Me by My Mother-in-law

Although the caguama is the largest of the sea turtles,
weighing as much as twenty arrobas [*]*, its flesh is not prized.*

When I met my mother-in-law, she was called Carmela, which wasn't the name she was given at birth. At the age of four, she was lost for several days, and her mother made a vow to the Virgin of Carmen that if she found her alive, she'd call her Carmen. On the third day, they found the little girl on an island near the far shore of the river, where caymans lurked back then. When I was a child the river was still wild, and I remember spotting manatees there. Carmela still swears she crossed that river in the arms of a tall, thin man with long hair who walked on the water. All the family was sure that the man who had carried her safe to the island was none other than Christ himself. Ever since, my mother-in-law has been known as Carmen. *Carmela.*

She told me another tale that was just as unbelievable. It happened before she was ten. A boy from the village fell in love with a local beauty, and she shared his love. They wanted to wed, but he was very poor. She was poor, too. Everyone in the village was poor. And he didn't even have work. Though they despaired, like all young people they also hoped. They didn't know what to hope for, but they had hopes. One day it dawned on the boy that the village had a past but no future. And so he and his best friend decided to go looking for fame and fortune. By a twist of fate, he found one but not the other,

---

* Twenty-five pounds.

though for a moment he thought he had found both.

The village's only source of life was the sea, so they went to the sea. But they didn't go to sea; they headed away from the river and the bay, along the coast toward Los Caletones. They knew that on that deserted beach, a giant sperm whale had once washed up and died. The men from the village had been drawn there by a thick swarm of black vultures (which was strange, because vultures shunned the sea). Despite the stench of rot, they had dug a great deal of sperm from the carcass, and had sold it for a top price in the capital. So Los Caletones held promise.

But they scoured the beach and found only driftwood and seaweed. Feeling beaten, they turned back toward home—the boy who wanted to marry feeling more beaten than his friend who didn't (or not right away, anyway). Searching for a spot where they could cross the dunes, they caught sight of a *caguama*. And by then they knew some things you don't about *caguamas*.

A reptile like the cayman, the caguama (the native name for the giant sea turtle) moves well in water (rivers and seas), but struggles on land. The sea being its natural element, it can pass hours under water without coming up for air. Once the female has reached the sea, she will return to land only to lay her eggs. The male never returns. Caguamas are slow on land because their paws have turned to fins, and because they often weigh as much as a ton. Some measure two yards broad by three long. In the words of a zoologist, "bearing on its back both its armor and its home," the caguama has no need of Achillean speed to plow the seas. When she emerges from the sea, the caguama continues to swim: she fins across the few short yards to her nest. Like other reptiles, the caguama practices internal fertilization, and distinguishing the sexes is not always easy. In many species, it is nevertheless possible to identify the sex of an adult. When the female caguama has just laid her eggs, her sex acquires a curiously human aspect. It has always been believed that the caguama sees well but hears nothing, although the cry of certain species can sometimes be heard, especially during rut. Those who have come into close contact with caguamas assert that they possess a degree of intelligence otherwise known only in mammals.

They saw her at the same moment, and they had the same thought. The two boys looked a lot alike, though one was handsome and the other wasn't. One was as strong as the other, and when they wrestled or arm wrestled, it was an even match. Both liked performing feats of strength. They were the strongest boys in the village, though one was smart and the other wasn't. Now the smarter of the two boys had an idea that he didn't need to explain to his friend. They often had the same thought at the same time. And, right away, his friend assented. They would seize the giant animal as it slogged toward the sea. They would sell the meat, which wasn't all that edible, the tortoise shell, which wasn't real tortoise, and the fat stored beneath the carapace, which they knew outdid chicken fat. They would get rich. "Nothing beats *caguama* fat." So the saying went, and they made it their motto— though they didn't know what the word "motto" meant.

Now the *caguama* came to a startled stop. Not because it had seen one boy or the other, but because it had felt, through the pads of its paws, the tremble of shoes running toward it. Then the *caguama* sighed, not because it foresaw its end (*caguamas* sometimes live to be a hundred), but because on land these sea creatures often sighed. Some people thought that when they stopped, *caguamas* sighed out whatever was left of the force they had mustered to move themselves over the sand. But, in the thrill of the moment, neither boy heard the muffled cry of the beached siren. Or maybe one *did*. When they reached the *caguama*, which lay there, stunned by the commotion around it, they hooted and shrieked. Then, with what was left of their strength, they began the hard task of flipping the turtle. They knew that a flipped *caguama* couldn't move. That it couldn't get back on all fours without help. That a flipped *caguama* was as good as dead. For the two boys, it was better than dead: it was a sitting fortune. Flipped, the creature beat its fins in that exotic element— air—as if it were water. *Caguamas* aren't as smart as we are, they thought— though only one of the two was smart.

One boy, or maybe the other (they were hard to tell apart), offered to go rustle up the *rastra* that belonged to his uncle, who lived in the hills nearby. I doubt many of you know what a *rastra* is. A carrier used by natives of both North and South America, it served as the wheel they never had. All they needed was three poles, two set lengthwise and joined at one end, the third placed crosswise to bear the load. At the other end, they laid the poles on their shoulders and pulled. A simple but great invention, the *rastra* could haul a lot of weight. The boy went off through the dunes.

Meanwhile, the first boy watched the *caguama*. He knew it couldn't move, so he wasn't scared it would flip back over. But he was scared of being robbed while he waited there alone. He thought about the countless combs, cases, and other fancy goods that could be made from such a specimen. In the village, the *caguama* would be the source of untold wealth. And though hauling it called for brute strength, selling it called for skill. Though his friend could help carry it, only he could sell it and get rich and marry.

As he thought these thoughts, he studied the helpless *caguama*. Though the skin on her chest and belly appeared to be hard, its creamy color made it look silky and soft against the dark outer shell. Her underbelly merged into a strong set of fins, which rowed in the air as though she didn't know she was lying trapped on her back. *Caguamas* are dumb, thought the boy. The *caguama* stopped paddling and let out a big sigh. An all-but-human mixture of despair and defeat, the sound scared the boy. But he was more curious than scared and he went on studying the creature. The dumb, dumb creature. Then he made a wonderful discovery: her sex.

As a naturalist had noted, often after she laid her eggs (maybe from the effort spent quickly expelling dozens of eggs or some other natural cause), the *caguama*'s vagina sat open to the air. Exposed, in this case, to the eyes of rude observers. It looked virgin. Unlike manatees, *caguamas* had no hair on their vulvae. The boy felt his curiosity yielding to desire. He made his decision, or it was made for him. He would fuck the *caguama*, a hot, ready female, right then and there. He looked around with a last trace of shame. He saw no one. The Los Caletones beach was always empty. It would take his friend some time to get back with the *rastra*. The boy walked around the *caguama* once more. Sensing him near, the creature shuddered a little and then stopped moving. The boy approached its vulva, which was pumping with what looked like steady suction. The hairless little-girl vulva seemed to tremble where it was softest. Aroused, the boy opened his crude fly. There was no need to drop the shorts he was too poor to wear. He pulled out his long, thick penis, whose dark color set off the creature's white skin. Next to her, his penis looked less big. He leaned, almost sprawled, over the *caguama*. With one hand, his left (he was left-handed), he held the shell and, with the help of the other, he stuck his hungry penis into the huge vagina, which sucked him all the way in. Maybe because he had only masturbated and never had sex, he felt an immense, wild rapture. An animal bliss. Since he didn't know he was committing the terrible sin of bestiality, he felt happy. Seconds after he entered her, a sensation he felt everywhere at once, he had his orgasm.

When a *caguama* is in rut (sudden penetration right after she has dropped her eggs induces a sensation a lot like rut), she feels a clash of urgent impulses. One is passive: the passivity of the female when attacked by the male. The other is active: the need to complete the act of coitus once it has begun. The sex act is always performed at sea, where the pair is both weightless and weighed down by pressure greater than the force of several atmospheres. Sometimes *caguamas* mate in the Gulf current, where they can be spotted from the beach. Procreation is therefore often under threat from adverse forces. But nature, or evolution, or what you will, has provided the female *caguama* with a coupling mechanism that overcomes all obstacles. The female sports an appendage made of the same substance as her shell, but curved, and sharp at the tip, which serves to hold the male firmly in position during the sex act. As the male approaches her in deep water and tries to hold onto her slippery shell, the female keeps this hook or harpoon hidden from view. But then she quickly releases the hook from its sheath inside her, pinning him like prey. She literally stabs him from below and behind. Only the hardness of the shell (*chelone* means "armor") prevents the male from being killed, like the male mantis, during copulation.

The other boy was dragging the *rastra* back to the beach and happily flexing his muscles. He was almost singing. When he left the hills behind and came out of the dunes, he saw a pair that seemed more and more united the closer he came. Suddenly he was stopped, not by shame but by fear. What he saw he would never forget. He went closer. He knew the *caguama* was a passive creature, even tame, and although he didn't know what you know, he saw what he saw. His friend was lying sprawled on the turtle, bleeding above and below his pants: from his buttocks, his legs, his feet, and around his leather sandals. At a glance, the boy knew that his friend had fainted. He wasn't dead, although by now he might have died many times. Held at a distance by the fear, the horror, and the blood pooling in the sand, it took him some time to glimpse the strange weapon with which the *caguama* had stabbed his friend. An autopsy would have revealed that, although her spur had pierced the invader just above the base of the spine, the curve of its blade had sliced through the anus in a downward thrust, cutting across the rectum, shredding the prostate, and slashing one or both testicles, its pointed tip driving a second duct through the penis, making it twice as hard.

The other boy knew that his friend was badly wounded and that he was sure to die if he stayed on the beach. He didn't try to extricate him or move him. Not out of concern or compassion, but out of fear. He didn't know which to fear more: his friend's sure death or the danger of the *caguama*, now a horrific sight. He had an idea which, under other circumstances, would have meant salvation: the *rastra* would serve its purpose and carry his friend and the *caguama* home.

He pushed the *rastra*'s two poles across the soft, loose sand and shoved them sideways under the beast. With more brute strength than skill. When he had positioned the contraption, he tied it with the ropes he had brought from his uncle's place, lashing them firmly around the *caguama* and his friend, who was as purple and pale as death (the paleness enhanced his perfect features, which now looked etched on the face of the peasant). He began hauling his happy, unhappy load.

How the boy pulled the pair the eight leagues home from the beach is as strange as the tragedy that gave rise to the deed. Sometime after noon he reached the village, which lay as dull and still as ever. But (as it would in any village) this bizarre sight soon drew a crowd of villagers who were too shocked to react. They could have been attending a fair. The bride was among the last to arrive. For her, the horror of that day would never end. Yes, she knew her lover at once. What she didn't see was that there, before the crowd, he had opened his eyes.

But no one else saw it either. Because right then the *caguama* (like all immortal turtles) let out a cry which seemed to rise not from the throat of the beast but from the parted lips of the girl as she stood before her suitor. The boy on the turtle closed his eyes, and for a moment he dreamed of his wedding night.

Translated from the Spanish by Sarah Arvio

THEATER OPERA & SOCIETY

THE DIRECTOR'S PERSPECTIVE

PETER SELLARS

From a discussion in the Theater of Ideas Series at the Miller Theater and the Center for
Cultural and Historical Studies, Columbia University, October 22, 1996.

EDWARD W. SAID   *Precocity and provocativeness are the cornerstones of Peter Sellars's achievement as a
director, an intellectual, and an energetic presence on the world's stages. In the stunning,
astonishingly radical but nevertheless profoundly felt productions of* Don Giovanni,
Le Nozze di Figaro, *and* Così fan tutte *that he directed in Purchase, New York, in the
late 1980s,* Don Giovanni *was a drug pusher in Harlem, and* Così fan tutte *concerned
not two pairs of courtly lovers, but Vietnam veterans who were attempting to come to
terms with the difficult reality in which they found themselves. At the Théâtre du Châtelet
in Paris, Sellars recently directed a production of* The Rake's Progress *that was set in
an American prison. Contemporary settings are the hallmark of his style and he
continually challenges audiences to make the transformation from the rather remote and
frigid world of most opera productions into the world of contemporary reality. Sellars is
arguably the most interesting of all the opera directors alive today.*

I think the first thing that must be said about the director's perspective in
opera or theater is that when we talk about making theater, we're really
talking about making a society. Theater was proposed by the Greeks as a way
for a democracy to imagine how to organize itself. You needed a scientific
laboratory where you could say, "Okay, human beings get together in the

following ways: This works, this doesn't; this has a chance of working, this has no chance. How can we explore the possibilities without people losing their homes or being killed?" Theater was the way in which you could live through a catastrophe and still be alive to learn and tell about it.

What appalls me right now is the so-called Age of the Director. For the same reasons that people actually believed Ronald Reagan ran the United States government in the '80s, the director is constantly being promoted in the theater over writers, actors, and composers. To me, that's a pathetic delusion. It should be pretty obvious that the person nominally in charge is probably the most dispensable, and that as long as the people doing the actual work are good at what they're doing, something interesting is going to happen. A production has to be—like a government—a discussion among equals; and there has to be the kind of energy that comes from a democratically charged environment. That's the real task in my work, which is why I don't mind occasionally doing very bad shows. I truly don't care about show business. I care a lot more about democracy. I'm interested in what it will take to allow a conversation to happen among people. Some nights it happens intermittently. And with some shows there is no conversation, because nobody has found the vocabulary with which to have that particular discussion.

I think one of the crises in American democracy is that most Americans do not have the vocabulary to describe their lives, their desires, or their fears, because the culture that surrounds them is inadequate to those things. What gets expressed instead is the taste of a Big Mac. That's the language that's out there. And in this strangely mediated democracy, how can you arrive at a language that permits you not to have to shoot the person in front of you?

*I thought the problem was not that people don't have the words, but that they don't know what's the matter.**

The two things are, of course, related. I always think of the great Sufi mystic Rumi's statement that your ability to perceive increases with your necessity. That is to say, if you're an Eskimo and you really need to know that snow isn't just snow, it's forty different conditions, you learn how to describe snow. Rumi says, increase your perception by increasing your necessity, your need. Begin to understand how much you need, and how little. One of the most important parts of Sufi learning is abandoning your comfort zones and traveling as a beggar for ten years, thereby increasing your need and learning how much you can perceive once your perceptions aren't dulled by the material things you're clinging to.

In American culture, we can't put our fingers on what it is that's the irritant because we generally haven't been presented with a cultural manifestation that would allow us to describe it or recognize it. I really do believe in the Platonic idea that you are born with knowledge but you've forgotten it, and that being on this earth is about remembering what you already knew. The theater that moves you most deeply is not the Agatha Christie stuff—where you learn something that you never could have known and

---

* All of the questions appearing in italics were posed by members of the Miller Theater's audience.

that doesn't matter anyway. What moves you most deeply are the things that you already knew, that stimulate what Aristotle called re-cognition. You have lived your life in such a way as to distance yourself from something, but it's been looking at you for a while and here's an opportunity to connect with it. That's the big distinction between Sophocles and, say, Steven Spielberg as dramatists. The latter's work is based on novelty and surprise value, whereas so much of the truly great theater has no surprise in it at all. It has a shocking quality, but that's because most of the time, as you watch, you almost can't bear to look at the stage. You know too well what's going to happen. That's Eugene O'Neill's greatness: it's just unbearably clear what will happen in his plays—just as it is in your own family.

Theater is about setting up the conditions for recognition, and it evolved as a strategy for putting forward subject matter that the people in power didn't particularly want to hear: it's three parts charm, two parts daring, one part kamikaze flight. In America right now politics cannot be discussed in the political arena—just look at last year's Democratic and Republican conventions. The question is, if you can't talk about these things *there*, where can you talk about them? And what language can you use?

The way I tend to think of theater right now is that there is no discussion yet. I don't even think that this generation can have a discussion. I think of where we are now as being like the Vietnam peace talks—that first phase where they spent a year and a half arguing over the shape of the negotiating table. What shape of table would allow each person around it to feel that he was being correctly valued, heard, and represented?

Our question is: what is the shape of the table that will allow people in America to begin having discussions? This generation is searching for that table.

So we're not going to be able to produce a Shakespeare play in a way that will allow us to say we've covered all the ground in that play. Quite the opposite. You know the way the Wooster Group works or the way Jean-Luc Godard works: the actual subject matter of the performance is everything we don't understand about the material. What we don't understand about King Lear becomes the subject of the evening. We have no direct corollary for this material in our lives. Sometimes we wish we did; sometimes we're pleased we don't. But our relationship to it is a complicated one, and we have to be honest about that. A lot of the performances that interest me tend to be based on honesty, and the performances that send me running from the theater are ones in which people are just reciting lines they don't understand, raving on in dopey costumes, and making gestures they don't believe in, while the audience applauds—and perpetuates this weird conspiracy in which no one wants to admit that none of it makes much sense. . . .

Every time you're angry with the arts, you have to remember that they are just a reflection of the society in which they exist. It isn't bad theater, it's Washington D.C. A bad Shakespeare production is an afternoon with the Supreme Court, Bill Rehnquist presiding. For me, what's at stake in the arts is not the arts, and that's one of the things that has really depressed me about the National Endowment debate or lack of debate. What has damaged the arts in this country more than anything else is the artists

A scene from *Ghurba*, a play written by Shishir Kurup based on interviews conducted with the cast and members of the Arab-American community in Los Angeles, performed by the Cornerstone Theater Company at the L.A. Festival, 1993. The word *ghurba* means estrangement or longing, and is used here to describe the alienation of the Arab immigrant experience.

themselves—whose self-absorption and bizarre conviction that art is in and of itself *the point* are truly self-destructive. The only reason any of us are interested in art in the first place is presumably because we're interested in life, and art is a way of touching something in life that we can't get to otherwise. Once it is no longer a vessel for something, then it has lost its reason to exist. Of course the public votes to kill the National Endowment for the Arts. We don't need it, it's not helping us. It's just serving a small elite of people who like art for art's sake. So I think that the lines of those discussions—the way artists are trained and the way they think about themselves and what they're doing—urgently need to be redrawn.

Can you distinguish between art and show business? Do they have different functions? And are they both legitimate?

You're right, I'm mixing melons and kiwis here. One of the reasons I left New York ten years ago was so that I didn't have the art-versus-show-business anomaly in my mind all the time. There's this great tradition of art that supports itself because the public loves it so much that it creates cash flow. And there's another tradition of art that is supported through either a courtly or religious function—it's a way to spend money but it would never be expected to make money. I think those are both legitimate aspects of a society. There are some things in a society that will make money, and there are other things, such as the education of your children, that should not be expected to bring a return in dollars. Where that line blurs is a problem. Both things are urgent. Some people are gifted for the

type of pleasure function that makes money. God bless them, and I hope they keep doing what they're doing. They perform a real service. Other people view their work in a context that's more educational, or as part of a kind of spiritual armature or invisible structure within our society that helps to hold it together.

I think we have to become more sophisticated about our understanding of that second group. Valuing art for art's sake or turning the Museum of Modern Art into a temple is the worst thing that can happen. There's a very complicated tendency to "secularize" modern art, when most of it has its origins in religion. Igor Stravinsky's *Le Sacre du Printemps*, for example, was taken on as a great modernist cry and became part of this myth that modern art is about denying your ethnic background and claiming to be creating abstract art that comes from nowhere. In fact, at least a third of the numbers in *Le Sacre du Printemps* were lifted directly from ethnographic musical studies in the old Russian and Romanian. The critic Richard Taruskin has researched all of this.* When Stravinsky left Russia, he tried to become a cosmopolitan artist —with strange, Michael Jacksonesque results. When we go back and look at the roots of modernism, we have to acknowledge that pieces like *Le Sacre du Printemps* or *Les Noces* are very religious pieces. I mean, *sacre* means *sacred*. Their roots go much deeper than the modernist cliché of this century—and they have extraordinary mystical content.

There will always be the issue, for those of us who are still doing theater and even opera, of the

---

* See Taruskin's article, "A Myth of The Twentieth Century," in *Modernism/Modernity*, vol. 2, no. 1, 1995, pp. 1–26.

things we have to do to make money. Things that make money permit other things to exist. I suggest that artists begin to adopt a live-and-let-live policy. I had to figure out long ago, for example, that Mr. Pavarotti is my best friend: because he exists, Decca Records continues to put out my Mozart videos. So I'm not going to complain about show business. Artists are never as vicious as when they're discussing other artists. There is always this assumption that other artists are capable of all evil and must be stopped at all costs.

Is it possible to get out of this megalo-maniacal mode and into one that's more socially integrative? One in which we understand that, in the fullest sense of the word, every single person is multicultural, each of us has many selves, needs, and things that we can do? One in which we don't need this one-size-fits-none proto-fascist doctrine, where we can make art on a nonideological basis, or make art for our enemies? Until we do, nobody is safe. We have to find a way to continue talking, no matter with whom. The point is, God did not only create the people we like. He created a whole lot of people we don't like at all. And they don't like us. So what can we do about that? We have to engage.

What are the means of engagement? What is the vocabulary of engagement? And, in theater, dance, music, and opera, more than the words, what are the actions that speak? Can we physically commit ourselves to being with our enemies and dealing with them? Segregation is one of the most bitter pills of this period. One of the hardest things is being in Jerusalem with friends who refuse to join me for dinner in East Jerusalem or being with friends in West Los Angeles who refuse to join me for dinner in East

L.A. Most people in most cities in the world are frightened of their own city. They go to the same four places every day. What does it take to break through that wall of fear? I'm not talking global politics, I'm just saying, go ten blocks north. What does that take? With what kind of honesty can people who really disagree continue to live together?

Theater was created to address this. Opera was created to take it two steps further. Music is obviously the first step. Music is one of the only things that gets you through life. If we can't dance, we can't talk. In many societies, the chiefs are appointed for their skills in dancing and music, because the people who are outstanding dancers and musicians will have the power to convoke, to create an atmosphere, an environment, which permits movement on all sides.

Going back to the concept of art for art's sake, what do you think about the idea of creating art to piss people off as opposed to creating art to heal people?

I have a huge problem with the last two or three generations of art training and theater schools, which to my mind have encouraged the development of professional skills without any parallel encouragement of social or psychological awareness, public responsibility, or the human capacity for healing. The real basis of theater is not dealt with, and instead these bizarre exercises are performed. Despite certain extraordinary teachers, a large system has been put into place that simply grinds out theater professionals. The theater is now, to its shame, a *profession*.

Without wishing to sound too sentimental,

I'm very fond of theater that's done by people who don't get paid for it. Most theater throughout history has been put on by people who didn't get paid for it. And I welcome the art of the next century, without the National Endowment for the Arts, where the only people who will be left doing theater are the people who *have* to do it, no matter what. All the other flotsam and jetsam will be washed away because the theater will no longer be a career option. So, for me, the idea that in the next decade in America art will become samizdat, the equivalent of the underground art during the Brezhnev years in the Soviet Union, is not so bad. . . . You know, every night Pletsetskaya will dance *Swan Lake* at the Bolshoi, and every corporation, government, etc. will line up to fund it in the official palace of culture, while what's really happening will be happening in basements. . . . If you were in the Soviet Union in the '60s or '70s, you couldn't read about it in the newspaper. You had to know someone who knew someone who knew someone. You went there; it happened that night for the people who cared, and the people who didn't care weren't there. It wasn't about marketing, and it spread as a kind of a legend.

My theory is that most great theater is really bad, but important. There's a kind of spark. I'm sure the first night of *Ubu Roi* was awful, but weirdly important, you know? That's what theater is. It's not about eight billion hamburgers served. It's a legend that lives because it means something to somebody. That's the actual marketing.

So, in that sense, I'm not depressed about the current financial disaster in the arts. To me, art that isn't funded by the government or the corporations will have a different type of community basis. It will be produced on a small scale with direct interaction between artists and the people around them. That symbiosis is needed both to create the art and to fund it. Your great idea and finding money for it are the same thing. Does one thing actually drive the other in an interesting way? Is the discussion that you have to have in order to fund the work the discussion that should be on stage anyway?

You've been working in state-funded theaters in cultures that put a lot of money into art. How is it that you get around the very system that troubles you?

Obviously, I live a pretty bifurcated life. Something that I think is very important at this point in history, probably at any point in history, is that if you've only got one strategy, you're already dead. You've got to move in many different directions at once. I'm very fortunate to be able to work in very expensive places and be well supported, but I'm also subject to the pressures and censorship of those places. At the same time, through my work with the L.A. Festival and so on, I've been moving in the opposite direction, which is entirely toward community-based-and-supported art.

But I do regard myself as one of the last of the dinosaurs. I'm doing operas right now because I don't think there will be any opera in a few more years. I think the handwriting's on the wall for this stuff. There aren't enough people who are interested enough to come up with the kind of money that it will cost to feed those elephants twenty years from now. I don't have a problem with that. I think everything has its moment, and if it's useful it will come back later. One wants to

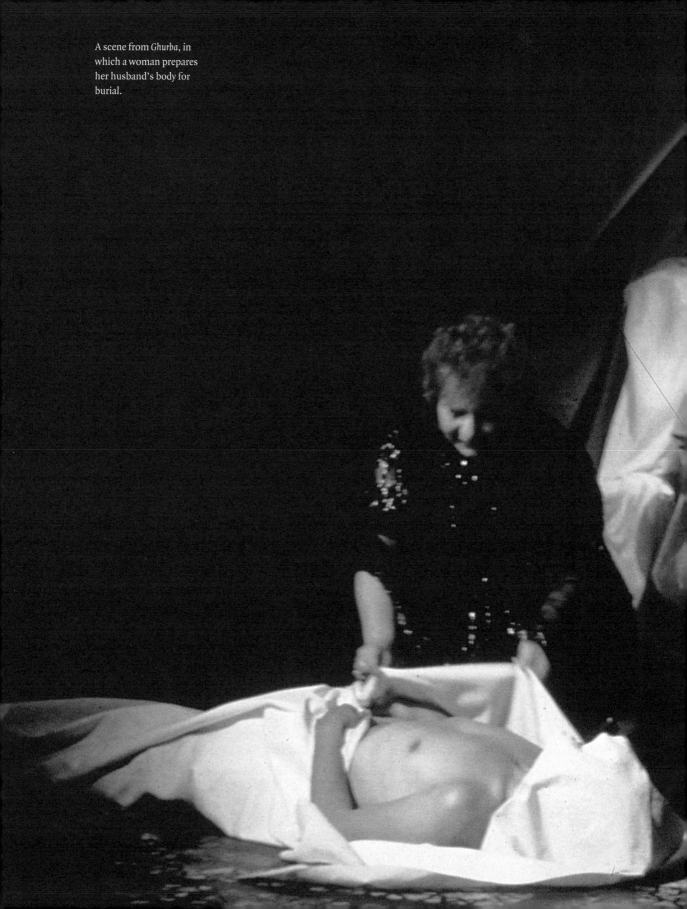

A scene from *Ghurba*, in which a woman prepares her husband's body for burial.

be intelligent about that and say, "certain things we care about, we want to keep them and we'll fight for them." On the other hand, the Buddhist principle of non-attachment may be better in another way. Maybe we should take these changes as a signal that our work should be taking other forms. I do feel equally called to do a show for rich people as to do a show in East L.A. Both things are important. One of the things I do with my expensive shows at Salzburg or Glyndebourne that nobody can get in to see is make sure that they get on television. Then they go all over the place and have other lives. That's what that kind of privilege will do. I think the big question is about the future of broadcasting, the Internet, and so on. All of those distribution and financial questions are about to be reinvented.

An artist might be very sympathetic to what you're saying about art for art's sake, but he might nevertheless feel some pull toward what seems to be essential, which is form. Even as he makes this socially committed public deliverance, there's a formal energy that is absolutely essential to what he's doing, and it has an autonomy of its own. So I was wondering what your view of form is?

I think it's something we struggle with every day. The dead letter of form is what we have in the United States justice system—a spectacular form with no life actually inside it. And there's obviously the crisis of organized religion at this moment. I think we have to look at form as something to be desired on one level but, on another level, as something that can become a real nemesis. God knows, in this century form has overtaken content in a way that's asphyxiating. One looks at parts of the world

where people are fighting for the right to vote and don't have the forms with which to do it, yet there you can feel the heat of commitment, courage, and invention. Here we preside over our invented forms with a kind of smugness, but don't bother to vote.

I think in art we face the same challenge. My work is elaborate—I'm an old-time formalist from way back, trained by the philosopher and linguist Roman Jakobson himself. So I deeply believe in form. At the same time, some of the most powerful, useful, and dynamic art I've seen in the last few years has been a formal mess—and its ability to be dynamic, to be many things in a very short span of time, was exactly one of the things that made it so valuable. I'm talking about theater work, for example, at the Cornerstone Theater Company or at the Los Angeles Poverty Department. The L.A.P.D. is a theater made up of homeless and formerly homeless people. Their shows are incoherent on one level—you never know who's going to show up and in what state; it has that Wooster Group energy. But, at the same time, the power of what's being said and how it gets said—and who deals with whom in order to say it—is always astonishing. It's an ongoing search for a means of conversation that doesn't exist. The Cornerstone Theater also involves a number of actors who have no professional theater experience. Their shows are a very complicated intersection of art and life and, again, usually a mess formally. But, as evenings of theater, you'll never forget them as long as you live. And, as a moment in that community's life, a real high-water mark. It's always tricky to assess these things, but my own feeling is that we're in a period of reaction against excessive formal structures and that we're moving toward something that is more flexible.

As you say, the crisis in the arts and in the theater is a reflection of the crisis in society. I sometimes wonder if it's a little grandiose to expect—as the avant-garde of this century has many times—to produce some change in society through the arts.

Picture whoever was on the cover of *Newsweek* this week, and then picture a Tibetan monk in a cave in the Himalayas praying for world peace. Who is going to help the world more? I think each of us has to do what we do, and if it helps in any way that's great. I think the important thing to know is that you'll never know what you've done. It's presumptious to assume that you could ever measure it. The Navajo idea is that we're working for the children of the seventh generation—that we're not going to see the results of anything we do in our lifetime. In two hundred years, it should matter that somebody now had the courage to do certain things which were unrecognized or opposed, but that will open some possibility for someone generations later. Mozart died thinking that his last three operas with da Ponte were disasters. He had a horrible time with that—they fell on primarily deaf ears—and I'm really personally grateful that he courageously wrote them anyway, so that two hundred years later I could stage them and use them to tell people what it felt like to live in New York in the '80s. It's like a wound: if you tear the bandage off every five minutes to see if it's healed, you'll get depressed and it will never heal. I think it's important to understand that certain things take time and operate in a way that you can't control or be conscious of, and

meanwhile you have to be committed and do your best in good faith. That's, of course, a hard one.

I agree with you, especially if you're socially committed. But my question was perhaps about the parameters that one can realistically set and what's possible.

What Bernice Johnson Reagon⋆ says is, "Take any position you occupy in life and radicalize it." Wherever you are, whomever you're coming into contact with, whatever that circle is, energize it and radicalize it. That's enough. Start with that and it will lead to something else, or it will be perfect and satisfying in itself. Theater is the art of whoever's in the room. Start there, and if you want more people in the room, go out and find them and ask them to join you. That's all theater is: who's in the room, whom you can interest in being in the room. And then extending that discussion.

I'm reluctant to join you in dancing on the grave of the NEA. For all its failure and bureaucratic compromise, it has established a democratization of culture that was unprecedented in this country. It was the catalyst for the formation of thousands of cultural organizations. Its demise, I feel, results in the collapse of such opportunities. I don't know that the social and economic conditions of this country will lead us to a samizdat culture. I fear they will lead more to the more classical cultural productions that existed prior to the NEA.

The amazing thing is that this country is like the

⋆ The founder and artistic director of Sweet Honey in the Rock, a cultural organization and vocal group dedicated to preserving the legacy and experience of African-American women in the United States.

hills in Southern California: they're brown and burnt, and then a little rainfall comes one morning and suddenly everything's green. A tiny bit of rainfall can go so far, and of course we're so parched culturally.

Over the last couple of years, the NEA has been unable to change anyone's actual budget. You spend more money hiring the grant writers than the grant is actually worth. It's become a nightmare. I'm a huge NEA supporter and I truly fought to keep it alive, don't get me wrong; but, for me, the most important thing the NEA did for the profession was to create a peer-based panel system, in which people flew all around the country and saw each other's work and created an unprecedented national discussion. And that was amazing. There was this shock, you know, as people realized, "oh, there is a lot going on out there, and before we make another stupid generalization, maybe we should actually notice that what's happening in Wyoming is important." So the NEA is really crucial, and I would love to have it back much bigger and much better. But it looks like we're not going to have it, so how can we react in a way where we're not just sitting around and telling stories about the death of kings? How do we mobilize? What are the terms of that mobilization, and what avenues does it leave open? I'm trying to take it positively, because if you take it negatively, you just get depressed. And, as artists, we're not allowed to do that.

Earlier you mentioned Russia and the underground culture that existed while Pletsetskaya was dancing at the Bolshoi. Don't you think there was already a preexisting language that allowed that samizdat culture to flourish? Do you think that stems from the fact that in certain societies, nonmonetary societies, you could call them, culture is seen as an alternative to religion? And do you think that part of the problem, specifically in the United States and maybe in countries like France and Germany, is that there is no spiritual alternative? For example, I saw your production of The Rake's Progress in Paris, and most people said, "oh, there goes Peter Sellars trying to be risqué and avant-garde and provocative." They didn't say, "there's Peter Sellars discussing a social issue."

There's a theory that rap music, for example, resulted when music programs were withdrawn from the schools: a generation without instruments created music anyway. The point is, you can't kill it. It doesn't matter what you do. It's built in. That's why, globally speaking, I don't worry about art going down the tubes. People will make it and, in fact, when it's made in response to certain necessities, its perceptual dimensions may actually increase. That part is not problematic.

As far as The Rake's Progress goes, yes, I'm doing an opera, so it attracts an opera audience, whatever that is. I hate to generalize about audiences, because you never know who's there and you never know what somebody's taking in or why. That's one reason why I'm always distrustful of discussions of the playwright's intentions. I've worked with plenty of playwrights, and they often have no idea what their intentions are, and if they do announce them, they're lying. Most audiences have no idea what they're getting. You feel certain things and after a while they sift through and you begin to put them together.

For whatever it's worth, I did build a big prison on the stage of the Châtelet Theater just

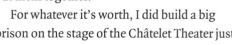

on the other side of the Seine from the Palais de Justice, where immigration detainees were being held in the prison before being deported. I was on every French television station, and I took the television cameras over there and said, "the prisoners in here are being deported next week," and then walked back across the bridge to the Châtelet where half of the people on stage were Africans. I did try to use the situation to address the specific crisis that was going on. And most of

The Rake's Progress, Théâtre du Châtelet, Paris, 1996.

the major media ran discussions on the topic, related to the show. I don't say that by making theater I'm going to change everybody's mind about prisons, but if everyone else also went to his or her place of work and brought up the topic, then at least it would get talked about. I think that's as much as anyone can do. Our task as artists is to respond, to make a record of

what's going on and to put something on stage that actually reflects society. The Koran says that God has shut the ears and the eyes and frozen the hearts of those he wants to lead astray into hell, and nothing you ever say to them will get through. That's a little severe, and if you're making theater, you hope that's not the case.

I would also like to mention another dimension of that show which is so important to me. It's not like an episode of "Nightline" that says, "Prison conditions are terrible and the government's response to immigration has been . . . now let's go over to John Allen who will tell us why. John, over to you . . . Well, I'm here in this appalling state. These people are sitting on the ground, they have not eaten in two days, and I'm in fact late for my lunch at the Intercontinental Hotel. What we have here is a human-rights tragedy. And back to you, Bill, in the studio." I don't think it's my job to have the final word or to correct everybody's misapprehensions. It's not about a quick fix or flash-flood reporting. It is about a certain type of immersion. I think I should bring these issues up in a context that is complex enough to give them dimensionality. If I'm able to do my work right, there's been an image or somebody's made a movement that will stick with you. And when this issue comes up later in your life, that moment can serve as a touchstone to remind you that it's not issues that are at stake, but people's lives. That's something.

It's not my job to be master of the universe, and I really do deplore theater that comes at you with that amount of arrogance. I try to keep my shows pretty perplexing. I really distrust theater that proves points and there's no way that you can walk away from one of my shows with a one-liner. It's the Sophoclean principle: something's only true if its opposite is also true. It's a more interesting dynamic. By the end of the evening, my point of view should have vanished and left room for the audience to explore what their points of view might be. You never know what kind of time scale that process is going to operate on, so I don't care if people like the show the night they see it. What I care about is whether, ten years later, there are still two images they can't forget. Each show is a handful of seeds that falls on different types of ground. What you hope is that some seed in some person's life finds some real soil and eventually produces a beautiful tree. It's not your tree. The seed was yours, the tree is theirs, and it's part of their garden. You have no idea how many of those seeds make it, and you can't fuss over that. You just do what you can. Some of the most moving moments are when people saw something you did and took it all wrong, but it doesn't matter because it has been useful to them. Whether they reacted positively or negatively, whether they understood what you thought you were doing or something completely different doesn't matter. That's why you must back away from all that egotistical stuff. This is not a popularity contest.

How do you relate the idea of performing in basements for small groups of friends to the concept of making something for your enemies and cutting through the zone of fear?

A lot of our work with the L.A. Festival was based on that question. The 1993 L.A. Festival took place one year after the Rodney King uprising, and five weeks of the Festival were held at the intersection where the first fires were lit, a place most people in Los Angeles would never dream of visiting. It took a year to prepare and engage the press, the police, the local residents, businesses, different organizations, schools, the audience, the ad agency, and so on. First we had to gain people's trust—the people in that area had been ripped off so many times by groups announcing that they were going to do something good for them. Every day, we were still making big mistakes, and learning and relearning basic human communication.

When we first visited Leimert Park with an eye toward locating a festival there, the bulbs in the streetlights had been burnt out for ten years. The park had not received any landscaping attention. There was a fountain but it had never been turned on. Garbage collection was sporadic at best. We were able to go to the City Council of Los Angeles and say, "Look, we're going to do a festival at this intersection, and the *New York Times* will be there." Bulbs were put in the streetlamps, the fountain was turned on, and the park was landscaped. I'm pleased to say that the *L.A. Times* reporters now run stories about that neighborhood regularly. It's become a bellwether for L.A. journalists and people just go there regularly.

That same festival included a lot of Jewish and Palestinian art, and we spent eighteen months working with people in different community contexts, planning the events jointly with the L.A. head of the American Jewish Congress and the Arab Anti-Defamation League. Our first scheduled protocol meeting was held to decide how to handle an evening when a Jewish poet and some Palestinian musicians were on the same program. That meeting lasted four hours. The two men had never met each other. They had a lot to talk about. But it took an arts festival to get them in the same room. They then exchanged phone numbers and now they do events together themselves. The point is to establish human relationships. Art in this case is a DMZ, a demilitarized zone, where you can step out of your official positions for a while, put down your weapons, and meet people.

The Festival covered some very serious topics—it did this fabulous double thing that art can do. On the one hand, people said, "oh, it's just art." So the mayor could sit there and listen to things that openly attacked him without being offended. If the same thing had come from a city council member . . . Yet, at the same time, it stuck with you. Art creates a different way of airing things that accounts for both humor and tragedy. I think our real task now is tone—what tone can you achieve that is heavy enough for us to recognize what we're carrying with us and that's light enough to allow us to continue carrying it?

For generations, one of the great pieces of the period, Mozart's last opera, *La Clemenza di Tito*, was thought to be unperformable because nothing happens in it. It's about a just ruler, Titus, who tends to the earthquake victims of Vesuvius. Then this weird plot hatches around him, and Act One ends with him almost being killed, the Senate building on fire, and the whole city in flames. (A completely undramatic piece!) In Act Two, he recovers and immediately, just like George Bush, and announces that he's going to search for the people who are responsible. Finally they are brought to him, and the opera ends as he forgives them and decides to found a government with them.

This next century is the century of Vaclav Havel and Nelson Mandela. It's the century of the people who tried to kill you for thirty years. Now we'll make a government together.

NAVIGATION

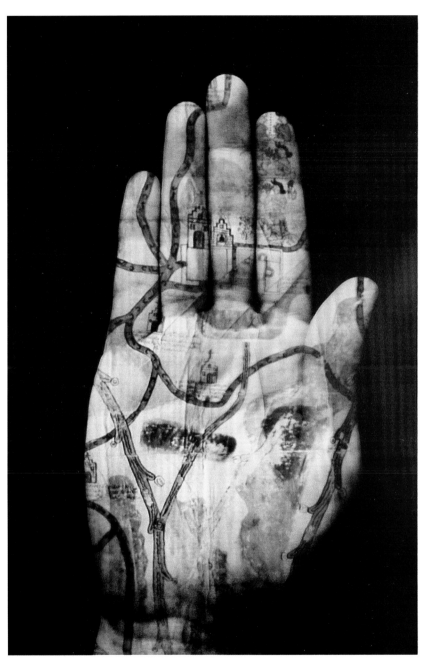

Tatiana Parcero, *Interior Cartography #36*, 1996.

Maria Fernanda Cardoso, *Cardoso Flea Circus*, 1996.

Jason Rhoades, *Spaceball*, 1997.

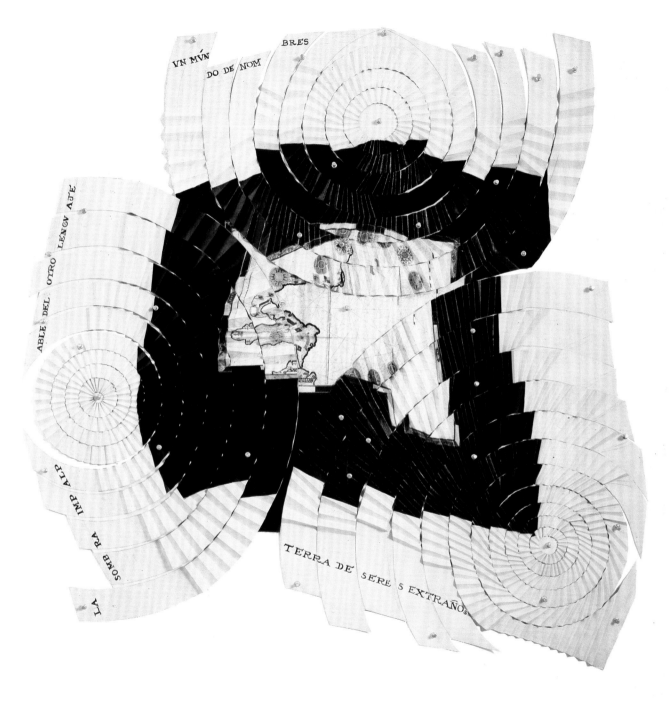

Miguel Angel Rios, *La Sombra Impalpable (The Impalpable Shadow)*, 1994.

KCHO, *Sea Wakes: My Cover, My Support* (LEFT) and *Infinite Column #5*, both 1996.

Jimmy Durham, *Forbidden Things*, 1993.

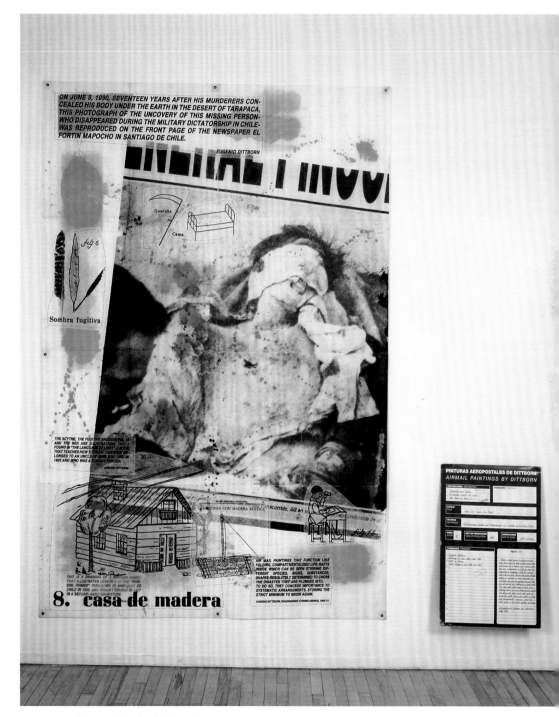

Eugenio Dittborn, *Have You Seen This Man? (Airmail Painting #92)*, 1991.

Ernesto Pujol, *Vuelo (Flight)*, 1995.

Pepón Osorio, *El Cab* (artist at work and detail of taxi interior), 1997.

Mark Dion, *Flotsam and Jetsam (the end of the game)*, 1995.

Juan Fernando Herrán, *Lat. 50° 02' N − Long. 5° 40' W* , 1994.

Manuel Piña, *Cuba*, 1994.

NAVIGATION

In the colonial imagination, navigation is perceived as the manifest destiny of the West. Over the centuries, Western literature has exalted the heroic achievements of those explorers, conquistadors, missionaries, and trading agents who have articulated the project of expropriation and the incorporation of the other into "civilization." Anthropologists and ideologists, sociologists and leisure travelers have then set out to convert these appropriations into fields of knowledge.

Not all of the ships have departed from the same port, nor have all of their destinies been alike. Yet the accounts of each navigation have been mystified and mythologized in ways that lent them historical universality and tailored them to fulfill and perpetuate colonialist desire. With their multitude of voices, these chronicles have nurtured the reader's distance and difference from the other, while at the same time seeming to bring the realization of his fantasies into the realm of possibility.

Contemporary representations of movement, place, and dislocation often acknowledge these colonial forms; and the practice of "navigation" in our modern global structure follows in the path of earlier flows of population, armies, goods, and capital—which, in the colonial era, tended to move "outward" from the center to the periphery, where people's relation to place was disrupted most frequently and radically. Thus, the so-called postmodern narratives of cultural intrusion and annihilation, forced subordination and adaptation, are not the result of entirely "new" epochal conditions, but are simply the products of a long history of confrontation between unequal cultures and forces.

The immigration explosion of the modern era, however, is primarily a massive movement inward from the periphery to the center. It has thus contributed to the Third-World-ization of the First World, destabilizing the modernist myth of navigation, while creating the phenomena of migrant workers, illegal aliens, refugees, and the homeless.

The majority of the people who navigate in our modern world are either on their way to work or on their way out of life-threatening situations. Yet tourism, that pursuit of a leisured and privileged class which accumulates culture along with frequent-flyer miles, is the world's largest growth industry.

The artists who have chosen to thread their way through these complexities to address the concept of navigation know that not all travels are voluntary, nor are all relocations an adventure, or all migrations a retreat.

OCTAVIO ZAYA

FROM THE WORLD OF MATTER

the given made here, the made, given

*

spilt October afternoon, half
winter, half late spring, dichotomies
of fallen and still clinging leaves

*

stain of leaves pressed to wet pavement
after the leaves are gone

*

pale blue rowing through green, lake
reflecting latening sky, then seen through
down to plankton

*

sun leaving its trace on water
when sun itself cannot be seen

*

leaves layered at the bottom of a clear still pool
two feet from the rising and subsiding
lake, stubbled shoreline broken off

*

diluvium, alluvion

*

square-cut well in cement, lakewater plunges
overflows from underneath
now visible, now submerged

*

brim and drain

*

lake, sky pieced together, meeting
of distinctions, blue-green to green-blue

*

worn jetty, pier defining cove, a bight, the water
pumping station another city at the horizon line

*

the filled-in fallen away to where, vanished
under landfill, lakewater, surge and stand

*

spray-painted slab of cement
sprawled across man-made rocks, structure
razed, dismantled, or someone tired of carrying it

*

half a mile on, smaller slab

*

texture, detail, a stretch of concrete smoother
than the rest, milky grain held perfectly
in focus, a Sunday's silver print

*

the aperture of afternoon

INSOMNIO

He had been dreaming of fiery steppes, of snares, of a sentry demanding safe conduct to let people through to a concave escarpment where the pounding of waves transformed the blaze into liquid smoke. When he opened his eyes, however, he found himself looking again at the rust of the oil rigs against the numbingly cold sky of Patagonia. He would have liked to know whether he had finally been allowed to hear the murmur of the foam, but lately he had been surfacing from his dreams through the pores of his skin, as the door closed behind him. There was no means of appeal, particularly as he slept in a position of crude foreshortening and the cold, the cramps, the delayed alarm for work all compelled him to linger on the edge of the material world. As if from an anchorless barge, he contemplated the shining, black mass of the Hotel Lobería, the twenty-two rows of Venetian blinds, many of them jammed, and the brilliance that the fake bronze beams rerouted toward the broken windows of the Sinardi bank. The hotel building was a functional fraud; perhaps that is why in the pink twilight of nightfall, beneath a veil of rust and soot, it would expand until its edges became feeble clay arches. Ezequiel, as if the day were vanishing discreetly, leaving its calling card, attempted to remember how old he was. The building recovered its rigidity. He thought that if he could halt the dissolution of that immense prism, he would not have to evaluate things all over again. Twelve years earlier—more likely fifteen or twenty—he had been a sort of notary of promise as well as a librarian, a compulsive lover of existentialism. Now he was one of two feverish men people sought out to write everything in the city worthy of being put onto paper: petitions to consulates, claims against neighbors, farewell speeches, parochial edicts, recipes, brochures. He had even written love letters from embarrassed prostatics. And given that he had vegetated in the city of Krámer as long as he had, it seemed to him that in reality, he had managed his destiny with considerable elegance. *Neither lack of willpower nor urgency, neither tedious memory nor fear of fright. Everything can be solved with a quick shake, as when a dog leaves the water under a lime-white moon.* In any case, the same desire to leave was mitigated at times—surprisingly—by his hate for the hypocrites who were making him wait. Almost grazing his eyelids, a group of South Africans jogged by in running suits. Despite being blond and solidly built, even insolent, they had had no choice but to hire themselves out as walking advertisements: all of them wore flashy prints of cigarettes and placards that read MAGISTRALES, TODAY'S SMOKE on their chests and backs. They ran around in the dusk, the South Africans, exuding a sorrowful distinction, and from a distance they looked like phosphorous heroes. All of them but the last one, a shorter man who ran with his sneakers untied and was going to trip at any moment.

Without leaning away from the bank wall, the lapels on his tabard sticking up, Ezequiel lifted himself high enough to survey the desolate panorama of the plaza. Although he hadn't seen it for years perhaps, although the city had interdicted it, the sea was close and at this time of day exhaled a smell of tallow and crustaceans. Braided into the wind, it came to impregnate the bellies of the telegraphic wires. *What do I want with this smell? What is the purpose of this view?* Ezequiel nodded to the manager who occupied the entire fourth floor of his building. He always forgot that the man was myopic. He did what he could so as not to fall asleep again. He didn't know if he fell asleep. On the small green patches of grass, among office workers in overcoats and hotel scullions, ten or twelve North American soldiers played soccer with a can of Heineken. They were on leave, or it could have been that their mission consisted in being on leave in the city. So little light remained that when the can went flying off onto the concrete esplanade next to the mayor's office, the shafts of night swallowed it up and the players seemed to caress the air like undisciplined dancers. On the other side, half hidden by the bronze monument to Krámer, several boys and a girl, sheathed in leather from neck to toe, swapped a king-size cigarette. On the sidewalk across from them, beneath the crooked canopy of the hotel, the line of street vendors was forming, an open and silent conclave that stretched before the facade of Our Lady of the Gulf as if waiting for the satellite-shaped bell tower to start spitting out a horde of customers. Except for the guard appointed to watch over them from a translucent booth and the owner of the restaurant El Nandú, who was probably afraid of them, no one paid them any attention. To the left of the restaurant there had been a vacant lot planted with thistle and columns; there were those still waiting to see it transformed into a cultural center, but it continued to be otherwise: nothing more than the field where a group of Portuguese businessmen, the sons of settlers expelled from Africa, had joined impotencies to construct an amusement park featuring the whip, a Ferris wheel, a house of mirrors, two stalls of target shooting, a wheel of fortune, and a tunnel of horrors.

★

In the back seat of the No. 20 bus, suffocated by a criminal set of heaters, the gentle brushing of a handkerchief against his bruises was enough to put him to sleep. The vinyl covers became velvet quilts, the linoleum on the ceiling became *caoba*, and the cardiac panting of the motor, a whistle of turbines. He was so thirsty that, in spite of his fear of paralysis, he decided to stand up without betraying the admiration of his traveling companions. As he walked across the carpeted belly of the airplane, the faces framed in the headrests began to lose their features as if a bricklayer's spatula had uniformly coated them with plaster. A stewardess with big hair who was wearing a shawl that bore a metal pin with the name Selva on it slipped him into the WC, but when he turned to embrace her all he found was a narrow staircase with open stairs. Little by little, he left the cabin below him to emerge under a nighttime dome spattered with stars, which at first accepted him and then began sucking at him with such force that his skin began to come off as if it were an onion peel. A boy not more than eleven years old who was secretly trying to light a cigarette with a golden Dunhill accidentally elbowed him and Ezequiel's cheek banged against the fogged glass. *Moved, he said to himself.*

This is called feeling moved. Otherwise what could it possibly be called. Cleaning the patch of glass with the sleeve of his tabard, he saw the ships of aluminum and bakelite from the Jacobici market, the protruding apses, fierce and shining against a forest of bent antennae. He hastened to climb down. Beside the transparent panels, spurred on by the smell of chickens, hake, and macerated fruit, the only actual crowd in Krámer surrounded the mountains of scraps. There were punks, widows, night watchmen, parents, accountants, chauffeurs, all the various outfits of poverty. Ezequiel bought a paper cone full of peanuts from a Senegalese woman, walked ahead with violent shoves among marine infantry giants and women with mesh bags and, drugged by the moderate tumult, he stopped before the enormous tubular kiosk where, adrift among videotapes and three-dimensional comics, newspapers from Düsseldorf, Chicago, Stockholm, Paris, Palermo, and Buenos Aires accumulated. There was something in these papers that would not permit them to be bought and it might simply be the mark of the outside world. Worse still: they contained depictions of the future, which in Krámer only had the outline of a day or of one chance and beneath that, nothing. And if, nevertheless, one listened to the news it was because those things did not cease to be events happening at the same time as other ones, a bee in a peony, a neighbor's sneeze, vanishing immediately. Thinking about this, he boarded a bus. It was painted blue and let him off at the end of Immigration Avenue, where the Futaleufú neighborhood bordered North, among half-empty concrete buildings, perpetually at odds with the uralite roofs of the preserves factories. Pursued by a thick fume of seasonings, then by the clatter of the looms, he walked down the Avenue of Work to where it ended at the edge of the factories, at the annex of the Brigade, a pretentious reserve known for its stables where ten or twelve abulic soldiers took care of the mayor's polo horses as if they were vestal virgins. It was neither a detachment nor workers' housing: it was simply an immense piece of land filled with clover and grass, ringed by a wire fence, and Ezequiel liked to gaze at it, leaning against a post, because the brown mouth of the desert would never devour it and because in the back, before reaching the paltry river, a curtain of slim poplars sheltered the parcel like warriors in a healthy land. As on other occasions, he was rewarded for his patience: two horses emerged from the pavilion in one corner. One of them, sorrel-colored and short-legged, trotted alone, receiving the threads of light on its hind quarters. It neighed and stretched its neck to nibble at the grass. The other one, a chestnut-colored horse that shone as if freshly bathed, was mounted by a chubby and unkempt soldier dressed in fatigues, who squeezed the horse's flanks for a while and then set it to trotting with long and limber steps. Ezequiel thought that a horse was a very beautiful thing. *And its muzzle slicing through the light is also beautiful and so is its lank tail and tousled mane and a man riding a horse.* Joined like that, one with the other, they did not seem so much an immortal engraving as a fable invented by the restlessness of the oil rigs. For the rigs, just like the clamor of the freight elevators behind Ezequiel, continued to exist, stubborn, taller than the poplar trees, stationed between crushed stone and uneven ground like an antechamber, not to the mesa, but rather to a border that kept itself hidden: radars, terrapleins, tanks, batteries, high-tension wires, or maybe not; maybe, he said to himself, nothing but horizon and endless fissures, copper-colored shrubs, dust clouds. *And a woman riding a horse? Why not? And a naked woman? And a female centaur?* A silver fighter passed by, flying low, spilling sparkle and din in its wake, finally vanishing from sight behind the deformed pyramid of trash harassed by hundreds of gulls. A chalk line scored the mass of clouds from north to south and a gush of sun slipped into the grass. The soldier pulled on the reins; saliva flew from the horse's mouth, slicing the air like sheets of diamond. Why didn't they leap over the fence in a single bound? *Why don't I, just as I am, start walking, piano piano, and see whether they grab me?* There was talk of people who had tried to leave on their own, slowly. Of course, no one knew how or where they ended up.

Translated from the Spanish by Mark Schafer

SONG OF THE ANDOUMBOULOU: 35

A last meeting after other
last meetings. Up what felt
   like a stairway a window at
which he sat overlooking
                              Lone
   Coast, his eyes' and the
   water's color the inside
      color of green grapes . . .
A last meeting. Another last
      meeting. Now in a mood
                              where
      if I said "struck" he
                        said "stricken,"
      the sound a song of wanting
   to have risen, flute-borne abrasion
   a sudden flight of stairs newly
                              right
side up. Where we had gone or what we
   had gotten . . . What the soul, again
said to have been a boat or been
      on a boat, grew wings and went
      down on all fours to go after,
                              cracked
alterity,   qu'ahttet kin . . . Up what
   felt like a stairway a window at
which he sat looking out at Lone
                              Coast.
   Sat myself down beside him. The
nay-player sat beside me . . .

   Whatsaid remanence. Whatsaid
      remit. What the nay said's
                        whatsaid

quaver, clipped reed an asthmatic
embankment, reach if not roll of it
missed by the names we knew it
by,   Brush,   Blown Host,   Ramp
                                        of
Heaven . . . All to say a ghost
had shown up we knew by more than
one name, Ahtt being not yet
erased, rearranged, rearrangement's
                                        intimated
eclipse. What, unaffected by
                            in-between,
inside was outside would be, wished
it would be, said it would be, said
wish made so . . . Spooked amanuensis . . .
Atthic recluse . . . Sat beside him,
                                        said
only, "So." As if "So" summed everything
up, it seemed I sighed. *Would I were the*
he they took me for, it seemed I said,
semisaid, half-said, half-sang . . .
I read from a book. I said only,
                                        "So."
The Book of Iridescent Dissolve it
seemed it was, bridge between "end"
and "again" he seemed intent on,
brine book, nay-strewn salt . . .
I said only, "So." "So" said it
                                all . . .
All there was to say went skyward,
thin ventriloquial smoke. What it
seemed I said, semisaid, it seemed he
                                        wrote . . .

It was a green book we made, yellow
book, red book, black tablet we

scratched in Wrack Tavern. Bits of

　　　　　　　　　　mirror

　　made it flash, fade, flash again,
　　strobelit, ythmic writ. A twist
　　　of cloth or an appurtenance of
　　straw bore gnostic import, known,
it was ours to infer, by none if

　　　　　　　　　not by

　　those who no longer spoke . . .
　　　Inductees into a school of scramble,
　　the altered state we rode in search of

　　　　　　　　　　　receding,

　　Emanon the something-out-of-nothing
we saw

　　　•

　　Sat straddling two extremes. Endlessly
　　gave names to what had none. One foot
　　on Lookout Ledge, the other on Loquat
Lift, flute furtherance a bank of mulled

　　　　　　　　　　air

　　we came to next, mulled air posed
　　as atavistic earth . . . Another meeting
　　which was another last meeting. Sat in
Qua Precipice's open-air café, looked

　　　　　　　　　out on

　　Lone Coast. Yet again spoke of his
　　Lady of the Loquat Tree . . . Claimed
　　she had forgotten more than we knew,

　　　　　　　　　knew

more than we knew, not known for knowing,
　　the train, bus, boat we'd been on
　　long borne away, said flute furtherance
　　ate away at Lookout Ledge. His was an

　　　　　　　　　I hers

ignited, he insisted, theirs had it
                              been his
     to give . . . All to say that two no longer
with us long ago lay side by side,
                              each
        the other's ordained exit each of them
        thought, there though if only in thought no
        less to be reckoned with, each
                              the
other's elegiac twin. So to say that we
                              whose
        flutes blew elsewhere weakened, they
        whose we approached revived, mythic
        repair borne by nothing if not by
                              breath
we took, nonsonance's nay-splayed
                              scut.
        Whatsaid ride into a realm of silence.
        There was a word we were told to keep
        to ourselves . . . The word was *rapture* and
it stuck in our throats, whose last resort,
                              we
     heard it said, was to be so
taken

———————————

Name Ad Nauseam stood in our way, was
our way, loquat coinage's wind-affianced
escort, exodus, flute-furthered,
qu'ahttet flight. At the sound of its
                     blowing
we bowed our heads, he who'd have been
    otherwise, we who were not . . .
                    Hung
in the air at T'bal's behest, we
   who'd been birds whose heads grew to
such music, hoofed instruction
                   borne
by Abakwa drums . . .
               Repeatedly scratched
at the paper we wrote on, Stra Choir's
laryngitic address . . .
              Flute furtherance's
culled undercurrent, stuck surrogacy,
                  felt
for the level on which to fade, utterly
                placeless,
skulls rapped by knuckles, aggregate
            fist

      ———————————

    Echoed an earlier echo . . . "Cuando
yo me muera," semisaid, semisung,
  cante jondo's bluff . . . "When I die,"
we half-said, half-sang. Worm in
                          our throats,
   inexistent smoke it came out of.
  Shook what could be said to've
   housed it, dream within a dream,
fraught forfeiture, fret . . .
                  Cramped
   expanse we crossed, came to
  Qua Precipice. A green book,
   red book, yellow, painted
scroll, read as we rode
                it seemed . . .
   Stubbled earth an extended
  braille we redacted, blind,
                 ythmic

rush, limbic
strum

NEWS FROM THE EMPIRE

Emperor Maximilian of Mexico, circa 1866.

Empress Carlota of Mexico, circa 1866.

> *Imagination, the madwoman of the house.*
> —PHRASE ATTRIBUTED TO MALEBRANCHE

I am Maria Carlota of Belgium, Empress of Mexico and of America. I am Maria Carlota Amelia, cousin to the Queen of England, Grand Master of the Cross of San Carlo and Viceroy of the Provinces of Lombardo-Veneto sheltered by Austrian compassion and clemency under the wings of the two-headed eagle of the House of Hapsburg. I am Maria Carlota Amelia Victoria, daughter of Leopold Prince of Saxony-Coburg and King of Belgium whom they called the Nestor of the Governors and who sat me on his lap, caressing my brown hair and telling me I was the little sylph of the Palace of Laeken. I am Maria Carlota Amelia Victoria Clementina, daughter of Louise Marie d'Orleans, the saintly queen of the blue eyes and the Bourbon nose who died of consumption and melancholy over the exile and death of Louis Philippe, my grandfather, who when he was still King of France covered my lap with chestnuts and my face with kisses in the Gardens of the Tuileries. I am Maria Carlota Amelia Victoria Clementina Leopoldina, niece of Prince Joinville and cousin to the Count of Paris, sister of the Duke of Brabant, who was King of Belgium and conqueror of the Congo and sister of the Count of Flanders, in whose arms I learned to dance when I was ten years old, in the shade of the hawthorns in bloom. I am Carlota Amelia, wife of Ferdinand Maximilian Joseph, Archduke of Austria, Prince of Hungary and of Bohemia, Count of

Hapsburg, Prince of Lorraine, Emperor of Mexico, and King of the World, who was born in the Imperial Palace of Schönbrunn and was the first descendant of the Catholic monarchs Ferdinand and Isabel to cross the ocean and set foot in America, and who ordered a white palace which faced the sea to be built for me on the shores of the Adriatic, and another day took me to Mexico to live in a gray castle that faced the valley and the volcanoes covered with snow, and who one June morning many years ago was executed by a firing squad in the city of Queretaro. I am Carlota Amelia, Regent of Anahuac, Queen of Nicaragua, Baroness of Mato Grosso, Princess of Chichen Itza. I am Carlota Amelia of Belgium, Empress of Mexico and of America: I am eighty-six years old and have spent sixty of them drinking, mad with thirst, in the fountains of Rome.

Today the messenger has come to bring me news from the empire. He came, laden with memories and dreams, in a caravel whose sails were filled by a single gust of luminous wind pregnant with parrots. He brought me a fistful of sand from the Island of Sacrifices, gloves of deerskin and an enormous barrel of precious wood overflowing with burning, foaming chocolate, where I will bathe every day of my life until my Bourbon princess skin, until my crazy old woman's skin, until my skin of white lace from Alençon and Brussels, my snowy skin like the magnolias of the Gardens of Miramar, until my skin, Maximilian, my skin cracked by the centuries and the storms and the crumbling dynasties, my white skin of a Memling angel and of a Beguinage bride falls to pieces and a new dark and perfumed skin, dark like the cocoa of Soconusco and perfumed like the vanilla of Papantla covers me whole, Maximilian, from my dark forehead to the tips of my bare, perfumed feet of a Mexican Indian woman, of a dark-skinned virgin, of the Empress of America.

The messenger also brought me, dear Max, a locket with some threads of the blond beard that flowed across your chest decorated with the Aztec Eagle and flapped like an enormous butterfly with golden wings, when on horseback, in your charro suit and sombrero encrusted with sterling-silver arabesques, you galloped over the plains of Apam amid clouds of dust and glory. I have been told that those barbarians, Maximilian, when your body was still warm, when they had barely sculpted your death mask with plaster of Paris, those savages tore out your beard and hair to sell those locks for a

few piasters. Who would have imagined, Maximilian, that what happened to
your father would happen to you, if it's true that barely a few minutes after
the unlucky Duke of Reichstadt, whom nothing or no one could save from
early death, not even the muriatic baths nor the love of your mother, the
Archduchess Sofia, had died in the same Palace of Schönbrunn where you
had just been born, they clipped all his blond curls to keep them in lockets;
but he was saved, and not you, Maximilian, from having his heart cut into
pieces to sell the scraps for a few *reales*.

Translated from the Spanish by Suzanne Jill Levine

VIEWS OF BRAZIL

MARC FERREZ

Dom Pedro II Dedicating the Rio de Janeiro
Waterworks, 1879.

Viaduct, Paranaguá-Curitiba Railroad, Province of Parana, circa 1879.

Praia d'Icarahy

Icarahy Beach, circa 1885.

Brazilian pines (Araucaria
Brasiliensis), 1879.

Rio do Ouro Reservoir, 1879.

Train to the Corcovado, circa 1895.

Pipe Laying, Marity Bridge, 1879.

MARC FERREZ

The years between 1859 and 1915 were among the most tumultuous and transformative in the history of Brazil. In the 1860s, Brazil fought a victorious but tragic war with the neighboring Paraguay that left Paraguay in ruins and established a new military class in Brazil. The abolition of slavery in 1888 brought freedom to 600,000 slaves. A brutal war was carried out against the Canudos in the far north of Brazil, and citizen riots erupted over the mammoth urban renewal of Rio de Janeiro in the early twentieth century. Emperor Dom Pedro II was the continent's last ruling monarch and, in 1889, Brazil declared itself a republic.

Considered by many to be one of Brazil's greatest artists and among the world's greatest landscape photographers, Marc Ferrez spent those years documenting his country's Herculean efforts to transform itself into a modern capitalist nation—as defined by European economic and social standards of the late nineteenth and early twentieth centuries. Although he photographed almost every city in Brazil, including the seaports, mines, railroads, plantations, and public works, as well as landscapes from the Pacific coast to the Amazonian interior, there is no evidence, in his work, of the tumult and contradictions of the time: the poverty and illiteracy of both city and country, the struggles over slavery, the clash of classes. Ferrez presented the world with a view of Brazil that focused on economic progress and unparalleled natural beauty. The sculptural elegance of his compositions, the careful use of light and scale, and his choice of subject matter pay tribute to the country's wealth of natural resources, its growing industrial infrastructure, and the architectural symmetry of its cities.

Born into a family of French artists who had emigrated to Brazil as part of a group of artists and academicians brought over to found the National Academy of Fine Arts in 1816, Ferrez was educated in Paris by a sculptor who was a family friend. As the urban renewal of Rio de Janeiro echoed Baron Haussmann's earlier reconstruction of Paris, Ferrez's documentation (1903–1906) of the Avenida Central and the rebuilding of Rio (1903–1915) parallels the work of French photographers Charles Marville and Edouard Baldus in Paris. His landscape photography shows a strong similarity to the work of the U.S. photographers of the western frontier, in particular Carleton Watkins. The photographs taken by all of these men reflect a world in which nature and technology were considered part of a passage to the future: nature enhanced by greater social utilization, and cities reshaped to feature a new order of civilization.

The importance of science in Ferrez's career is reflected not only in the subject matter of his photographs but also in his continuing experimentation with photographic technology. He made use of the new printing and film development techniques being marketed in

Europe, developed innovative methods of using X-ray photography and of photographing moving ships at sea, designed a new panorama camera based on the French Brandon model, and introduced Lumière's cinematographic projection to the Brazilian public.

One of his most remarkable images illustrates the complexity of the relationship between art and science in his work: The composition of the photograph, *Dom Pedro II Dedicating the Rio de Janeiro Waterworks* (1879), emphasizes the almost Grecian grandeur of the waterworks around the Emperor, while still focusing on the human being who brought it into existence. "It is like a stage set," comments Hack Hoffenberg, an early collector and long-time admirer of Ferrez's work. "There is science and surrealism in this image. Why would you lure an Emperor into the bottom of a waterworks?"

WENDY WATRISS

Entrance to Rio de Janeiro (View from Outside the Bay), circa 1880.

GABRIELA MISTRAL

THEY TALK ABOUT YOU

They talked to me about you, staining you with numerous words. Why wear out uselessly the language of men? I closed my eyes and I watched you in my heart. And you were pure, like the frost that dawns asleep in the crystals.

They talked to me about you, praising you with numerous words. Why wear out uselessly the language of men? . . . I remained silent, and the praise rose from inside, luminous as when the mist rises from the sea.

They silenced your name the other day, and they said others in ardent glorification. The foreign names descended on me, ruined. And your name that nobody pronounced was present, like the spring that fills the valley, though no one was singing it.

HIDE ME

Hide me, so the world cannot see me. Hide me as a trunk hides its resin, so I can perfume you in shadow, like a drop of sap. I could soften you with it, and others would not know where your sweetness comes from. . . .

I look ugly without you, like something deprived of place, like roots abandoned on earth.

Why am I not small, like an almond in its closed shell?

Make me into a drop of your blood, and I will travel through your face; I will be the brightest point on a grapevine. Make me your breath, and I will move in and out of your chest; I will become red in your heart; I will rise into the air so I can enter you again. And I will be in this game all of my life.

Translated from the Spanish by Fatima Mujčinović

The Little

RED DEVIL

Once upon a time there was a little boy called Ángel, who lived in the cordillera of the Andes, at the edge of a lake. He lived with his aunt, who was ill; Ángel had also been ill, when he lived in Buenos Aires with his family. But there, in the cordillera, the exercise and the life in the open air had cured him of everything. He had become a little boy with a strong heart who loved violent games, as do almost all little boys who will later become powerful men.

One afternoon, when Ángel was roaming through hills and dales, the sky suddenly turned yellow, and the cows started to run, bellowing with fright. The trees and even the mountains started to sway, and the earth at Ángel's feet broke into a thousand pieces like glass. The boy, who was pale with fear over the earthquake, suddenly noticed, in the deep chasm that had opened up before him, a small, red creature that was scaling the wall of the crevice. At that moment, the large fissure closed again, and Ángel heard a very faint cry. Curious, he knelt down and saw the strangest thing in the world: a little devil, nothing less than a real, live, tiny, red devil that was no bigger than the finger of a six-month-old baby. The little devil was wailing with pain because the fissure had pinched his hand as it closed, and he was jumping up and down, looking up at Ángel with his pretty, terrified, little devil's face.

The boy picked him up by the tip of his tail and held him up, upside down. When he had examined him thoroughly, he said:

"Listen, little devil, if you are very good (because there is such a thing as a good devil), I will take you home and give you something to eat; but if you are a bad devil, I'll swing you around by your tail and throw you right into the middle of the lake."

Hearing this, the little devil started to laugh. "What an idea!" he said. "I am a friend to people. No one likes people as much as I do. I live in the fire at the center of the earth, but I've had enough of wandering around volcanoes all the time, and I decided to leave. I want to have a friend to play with. Would you like me to be your friend?"

"Very much!" said Ángel as he stood the little devil on the palm of his hand. "But promise you'll never do anything to hurt me. Pay attention, or you'll regret it, you devilish little devil!"

"What an idea!" the little devil said again, holding out his hand. "Friends forever! You'll see!"

Thus Ángel and the little devil became friends, lived like brothers, and embarked together on some surprising adventures.

Of course the little devil knew how to do all kinds of things and could play all kinds of games, but his great passion was for machinery. On a corner of the table where Ángel did his homework in the evening, the little devil set up a forge, complete with metals, tools, crucible, and some bellows for the fire. But it was all so minuscule that the entire workshop was barely the size of a dime; it was, however, complete, and there the little devil could make the delicate instruments he needed. And while the boy studied by lamplight, the little devil worked in the shadow of the lamp shade, hammering and blowing on the fire with admirable skill.

What was the little devil doing? What was he making? Ángel didn't know. It was all so tiny!

But the most amazing part of the story is that the little devil was invisible to everyone but Ángel. Only his young friend could see him; he was invisible to everyone else. The little red devil, however, did exist—as he would soon prove.

One afternoon, there was a catapult contest between the boys at school. The elastic of Ángel's catapult broke on the first shot, but just as he had resigned himself to losing, the little devil climbed onto his thumb.

"Don't worry, cousin," the little devil said. "Spread your thumb and your index finger so that I can hold onto them, then pull me hard by the tail; you'll see that I make the best catapult you've ever had."

Ángel did what the little devil told him, put a rock on his tail, pulled, pulled as far as he could and, sure enough, the rock whistled away so fast that he could still hear it whistling for a long time. Needless to say, Ángel won the contest.

Notice that the little devil called Ángel "cousin." The truth is that all men are cousins really, and they have even stranger relatives, as we will soon see.

Another time, the schoolmaster scolded Ángel unjustly; he said so many unpleasant things that, that same evening, as the little devil was working in his forge, Ángel, instead of doing his homework, put his head on the table and started to cry. The little devil noticed and said to him, laughing, "Don't worry, cousin! I'll get even with your schoolmaster. You'll see tomorrow."

Beating doubly hard on his anvil, he built a strange-looking machine and ran out carrying it. Still running, he arrived at the house of the schoolmaster, who was fast asleep, snoring. The little devil climbed very carefully into the schoolmaster's mouth, and placed the machine underneath his tongue.

What strange hinge could he have made? No one ever knew, but, during class the next day, the schoolmaster started to stutter as though he had a spring in his tongue. He tried to say: "Student Ángel!" but all he could say was, "St . . . u . . . u . . ." And the angrier he became at not being able to speak, the more his tongue stumbled over "St . . . u . . . u . . ." And the students jumped up happily onto their benches and shouted: "Mr. St-u-u! Mr. St-u-u!"

Another time, an evil man arrived in the village, with a hat pulled down so far over his eyes that only his mouth and the tip of his nose were visible. The assassin told everyone that he was going to kill Ángel as soon as he came out of his house because the boy had stolen his hen.

It was a lie; but that night as Ángel was crying, with his head on his arms at the table, the little devil, who was working in his forge, called to him, laughing: "Don't worry, cousin. Wait and see what fun we'll have with that brute tomorrow."

Just like the time before, he fashioned an instrument on his anvil and ran off to the house of the evil man, who was sleeping, climbed onto his forehead and, with the drill he'd made, he pierced a hole in the man's head.

It's easy to imagine how small the hole must have been; but it was big enough for the little devil. After he'd set the tip of his tail on fire with a match, he inserted the ashes, which had the power to drive the man insane. When the man woke up the next morning, he was crazy and, instead of killing Ángel, he ran through the streets ecstatically, declaring himself a Plymouth Rock hen; he crouched down, cackling, at each intersection and tried to lay an egg.

So the little devil had the power to do many things. The only thing that seemed to bother him was the heat, and he bathed eight or ten times a day in a glass.

In his forge, he had made a little gold comb and, crossing his legs on the rim of the glass, he slowly combed his hair, while playing in the water with the tip of his tail.

The little devil continued to perform services for his cousin Ángel, but the greatest of all was when he saved from death the boy's young sister, who lived in Buenos Aires. When Ángel heard that she was sick, he was so inconsolable that he didn't even want to get out of bed; and when he did get up, he would fall right back down, fully dressed, in tears. But the little devil managed to cheer him and they decided to walk to Buenos Aires, as they didn't have any money; and as they didn't know the way, the little devil kept his bearings by following the almost imperceptible fissures left by earthquakes, fissures that no one could see but the little devil, who had been born in the volcanoes at the center of the earth.

It would really take too long to recount all the adventures they had during this thousand-mile trek. But they did finally arrive in Buenos Aires; they reached the city just as Ángel's young sister had given up and was on the brink of dying.

The little devil understood when he saw her that this battle would be much harder than the ones he had waged against the stuttering schoolmaster and the madman, because now he had to fight against Sickness; and Sickness is the favorite daughter of Death. And what was he but a poor little devil? But we'll soon see if he was as poor as he said he was.

Sickness, as we said, is Death's favorite daughter, and the most intelligent of her daughters, although the most silent, pale, and thin. When Death wants to take someone away from the world, she makes use of train derailments, shipwrecks, car accidents, and all sorts of other surprise attacks.

But when the people chosen by Death are very cautious and stay locked up at home, then Death sends out her most silent, intelligent daughter, and Sickness gently opens the door and enters.

Knowing this, we can easily understand that Sickness, who had been wanting to carry off Divina (Ángel's young sister) for two months, would never leave the girl's bed. Sickness would arrive as night fell, without anyone seeing her. She would lay her hat and gloves on the nightstand, untie her hair, lie down next to Divina, and wrap her arms around her. Then the girl's sickness would deteriorate, her fever would rise, and she would become delirious. At eight o'clock in the morning, Sickness would get up, fix her hair, and leave. In the evening, she'd be back, and no one would see her come or go.

That was the situation. Ángel and the little devil had barely entered the room when Sickness arrived. She gently removed her hat and her gloves, and just as she was pulling back the sheets to lie down, the little devil, as quick as lightning, fastened Sickness's ankle with a thin chain of diamonds he'd made, and tied the other end to the foot of the bed. When Sickness tried to lie down, she couldn't move her leg.

Surprised, Sickness turned her head and saw the little devil who was sitting cross-legged on the back of a chair, laughing softly, with a finger to his lips.

"Ha ha! You weren't expecting this, cousin!" the little devil said to her. He also called Sickness "cousin," because people, devils, and sickness are all cousins.

Sickness frowned, knowing that she had been defeated. She didn't even try to move her leg, because the diamond chains that devils make can't be broken. The little devil had been stronger than her, and she was beaten. She could no longer lie down with her arms around Divina, because the girl would now notice her right away. So she said to the little devil: "Very good, cousin. Your power has overpowered mine, and I surrender. Untie me."

"Patience, cousin!" said the little devil, laughing and playing with his tail. "You're in such a rush! I will untie you when you have sworn to stop bothering Divina, who is the sister of my cousin Ángel, whom I love as much as I love myself. Do you swear?"

"I swear," said Sickness; and the little devil freed her. But instead of untying the knot in the chain, he cut it with his teeth.

When Sickness realized that she was free, she smiled strangely as she combed her hair; then she said to the little devil: "You have beaten me, cousin. But do you know that whoever opposes the plans of my mother Death, as you have, must die himself? You have saved this child, but it's you who will die now, immortal devil or not, do you understand?"

"Yes, I understand! I understand, cousin!" answered the little devil. "I know that I'm going to die, but I am less worried about it than you think. And now, my thin and pale cousin, will you do me the favor of leaving?"

Thus spoke the little devil. Two weeks later, Divina had completely recovered her health, and the roses of life colored her cheeks. But the little devil was dying: he no longer spoke or moved, and he spent all of his time in the garden. In the house, however, no one knew that Divina owed her health to the little devil, who had sacrificed his own life to save her. No one knew except Ángel; and Ángel, sitting on the sand, cried next to the dying little devil. He asked the little devil to let his young sister see him, so that she could thank him, at least, for what he had done for her. Because we mustn't forget that the little devil was invisible to everyone but Ángel.

The little devil, who knew that he was dying, consented, and Ángel ran off to find his sister; he came back with Divina. Seeing the sweet, intelligent, and good little devil, who was dying, curled up in a ball on the sand, she felt a deep compassion for him and, leaning over him, she kissed him on the forehead. Barely had the little devil felt the kiss when he was transformed into a young and handsome man. He jumped up, smiling, and said: "Thank you, cousin!"

Who could have imagined such a miracle? You will understand, however, when you realize that Ángel's young sister was not eight but seventeen and was also a very beautiful young woman. And since the beginning of time the kiss of a beautiful girl has had the power to transform a devil into a man, or vice versa; but this observation is really for the grown-ups.

The little devil had to end his life as a little devil, but not as a man; and thus he was able, once again, to outsmart Sickness.

Needless to say, Divina and her new cousin, the handsome young man, fell in love immediately. As for Ángel, after several years, he found himself one afternoon, sitting in the garden and thinking sadly that he would no longer have a little devil to help him along in life. As he mulled over this thought, he felt on his shoulder the hand of the ex-little devil, now his cousin and brother-in-law, who said: "Don't worry, cousin! You no longer need anyone to help you but yourself. As long as you were a child, I helped you because you didn't have the strength to fight for yourself. Now you are a man; and your strength of character and your heart, my cousin, are the little devils that will help you now."

Translated by Deborah Treisman with Kristina Cordero

T. J. ANDERSON III is a poet, who lives in Binghamton, New York. His translations from Aimé Césaire's *Soleil cou-coupé* are a collaborative effort with Richard Lanoie, a French-Canadian writer, and Thierry T. Gustave, a French teacher from Martinique.

REINALDO ARENAS was born in a small town near Holguín, Cuba, in 1943. In 1962, he won a scholarship to attend university in Havana, where he wrote his first novel, *Celestino antes del alba*, which was published in 1967 by the UNEAC (the National Union of Cuban Writers and Artists). Deeply impressed by the autobiography of the eighteenth-century revolutionary, Friar Servando Teresa de Mier, who spent most of his life fleeing intellectual persecution, Arenas wrote a fictional account of his life, titled *El mundo alucinante*, in 1966. When the manuscript was rejected by the Cuban authorities, Arenas had it published in France and Mexico, and it has since been translated into several other languages. The foreign publication of this book, however, was viewed as counterrevolutionary by the Cuban government, and in 1970 Arenas was sent to perform forced labor on a sugarcane plantation. His next two novels, *El palacio de las blanquísimas mofetas* and *Otra vez el mar*, were also written in secret and smuggled out of Havana. When he was released in 1976, he was forbidden to write. In 1980, Arenas was able to escape to the United States, where he published several more books and taught as a visiting professor at Florida International University, Miami, and at Cornell University. He died in New York in 1990. *The Glass Tower* was translated and excerpted from his collection *Adiós a Mamá* (Ediciones Universal, Miami, 1996).

SARAH ARVIO is a poet and translator. The publications her poems have appeared in include *The New Yorker*, *The Yale Review*, and *The Paris Review*, which awarded her the 1997 Bernard F. Connors Prize. She has translated novels, stories, essays, and poems. In 1992, she was awarded a NEA Translator's Fellowship. Her most recent translations are a selection of stories from the Spanish for *The Oxford Anthology of Latin American Short Stories*, to be published by Oxford University Press in the fall of 1997.

ADOLFO BIOY CASARES was born in Buenos Aires in 1914. He published his first miscellany, *Prólogo*, at age fifteen, and wrote and published five more books before the age of forty. A member of the Argentine literary sphere that centered around Victoria Ocampo, editor of *Sur* magazine, and Jorge Luis Borges, Casares collaborated with Borges on several works, including *Seis problemas para Don Isidro Parodi* (1942), *Dos fantasías memorables* (1946), and *Crónicas de Bustos Domecq* (1967). In 1940, Casares and Borges compiled the *Antología de la literatura fantástica* (Anthology of Fantastic Literature), which introduced a group of talented young Argentine writers, including Julio Cortázar, Victoria Ocampo, H. A. Murena, and José Bianco, to the rest of Latin America. Casares's own solo works include *La invención de Morel* (1940), *El sueño de los heroes* (1954), *Historia prodigiosa* (1956), *Diario de la guerra del cerdo* (1969), *Dormir al sol* (1973), and *La aventura de un fotógrafo en La Plata* (1985). In 1991, he was awarded the Premio Cervantes in Spain and the Premio Alfonso Reyes in Mexico. He lives in Buenos Aires.

GUILLERMO CABRERA INFANTE was born in Gibara, Cuba, in 1929. His parents founded the Cuban Communist Party and were temporarily imprisoned in 1936. In 1950, Cabrera Infante enrolled at the School of Journalism in Havana, and, a few years later, became the film critic for the magazine *Carteles*. In 1962, he was named the cultural attaché to Belgium. Returning to Cuba only once, for his mother's funeral, he settled in London in 1967, as the Spanish authorities would not grant him residency in Spain. He has since collaborated on several film projects, including the screenplays for *Vanishing Point*, *Under the Volcano*, and *The Lost City* (*La ciudad perdida*). In 1995, he was awarded the XII Premio Literario by the Instituto Italo-Latino Americano in Rome. His books include *Tres tristes tigres* (1967), *Exorcismos de esti(l)o* (1976), a homage to Raymond Queneau, *La Habana para un Infante difunto* (1979), and *Holy Smoke* (1985).

DAN CAMERON has lived in New York since 1979. He has curated exhibitions throughout Europe and the United States and writes regularly on contemporary art. Since 1995, he has been senior curator of the New Museum of Contemporary Art, where he is preparing a March 1998 exhibition of Doris Salcedo's work.

JUAN CAMERON was born in Valparaíso, Chile, in 1947. In addition to twelve books of poetry, he has written literary criticism and has translated work from Swedish, English, and Portuguese. He has won a number of literary prizes, the most recent being the 1996 First Prize for Poetry awarded by *El Mercurio*, Santiago, and the 1996 Valparaíso Municipal Prize for Literature. His bilingual collection, *Si regreso/If I Go Back* (Cross-Cultural Communications) was published in 1993. Although he lived and worked in exile in Malmö, Sweden, for much of the late 1980s and 1990s, he returned to Chile in March 1997.

AIMÉ CÉSAIRE was born in Martinique in 1913, and went to Paris to study in 1930. There, he met the African poets Léopold Senghor and Léon Gontian Damas, with whom he formulated the concept of *négritude*, an idea and a movement that encouraged blacks to accept their African heritage and embrace a culture independent of that imposed by French colonials. Césaire returned to Martinique in 1939, and began a political career first as a Communist and later as the leader of his own party. Often surrealist in their imagery, Césaire's poems include *Return to My Native Land* (1947) and *Ferrements* (1960), and his plays *The Tragedy of King Christophe* (1963) and *A Season in the Congo* (1966). He lives in Fort-de-France, where he has retired from his posts as Mayor and Deputy to the French National Assembly. The two poems published in this issue of *Grand Street* originally appeared in his collection *Soleil cou-coupé* in 1948; when that book was assimilated into *Cadastre* (1961), however, thirty-one poems—these among them—disappeared and were only recently reprinted in Césaire's *La Poésie* (Editions de Seuil, 1994).

RONALD CHRIST lives near Santa Fe, New Mexico, where he works as an editor, translator, and writer. He is currently finishing a critical study of the Argentine painter Marcelo Bonevardi, to be published by the University of Texas, and his most recent translation is *The Architecture of Josep Maria Jujol* (Lumen Books). His translation of Diamela Eltit's novel, *E. Luminata*, will be published by Lumen Books in the fall of 1997.

MARCELO COHEN was born in Buenos Aires in 1951. From 1975 to 1995, he lived in Barcelona. He has worked as a musician, an academic, a journalist, and a translator. His essays and articles on literature, culture, and politics have been published in such newspapers as *El País* (Madrid), *La Vanguardia* (Barcelona), and *Clarín* (Buenos Aires). He is the author of two books of short stories, *El buitre en invierno* and *El fin de lo mismo* (Anaya & Mario Muchnik), and of six novels, including *El país de la dama eléctrica*, *Inolvidables Veladas* (Minotauro), and *Insomnio* (Muchnik), from which the two selections published in this issue of *Grand Street* are excerpted. He is currently writing a book of two novellas, tentatively titled *Zonas raras*. He has translated the works of Jane Austen, Henry James, F. Scott Fitzgerald, and William S. Burroughs into Spanish. In 1995, he received a Guggenheim Fellowship for his fiction writing. He lives in Buenos Aires.

MIKE DAVIS is finishing a book on Los Angeles's recent trial by riot, flood, and earthquake titled *Ecology of Fear*. He is a contributing editor to *Grand Street*.

FERNANDO DEL PASO was born in Mexico in 1935. The recipient of two Guggenheim Fellowships, he moved to Europe with his family in 1972, and lived in London until 1986. Exhibitions of his paintings have been held at the Institute of Contemporary Art, London, and at the Galería Juana Mordó, Madrid. He has served as Consul General of Mexico in France. Del Paso has published three volumes of poetry, as well as the novels *Palinuro de Mexico* (Plaza & Janés, 1977), which won the Rómulo Gallegos Award in 1982 and the award for Best Foreign Novel in France in 1985, and *Noticias del imperio* (Plaza & Janés, 1987), from which the passage published in this issue of *Grand Street* was excerpted.

CARLOS DRUMMOND DE ANDRADE was born in Itabira, Brazil, in 1902. Expelled from a Jesuit school in Rio de Janeiro for "mental insubordination," he eventually graduated with a degree in pharmacology and, until his retirement in 1966, worked as a civil servant in the Ministry of Education. During that time, he also worked as a translator, essayist, short-story writer, and poet, and was a member of the Semana de Arte Moderna, a group of avant-garde poets formed in the 1920s. He died in 1987. A selection of his poems, titled *Travelling in the Family* (Random House/Ecco Press, edited and translated by Thomas Colchie and Mark Strand) was published in 1986. The poems published in this issue of *Grand Street* were translated from his volume *O Amor Natural* (Círculo do Livro).

DIAMELA ELTIT was born in Santiago, Chile, in 1949. The author of several novels and essays, she won Chile's Institute of Letters Prize in 1996. That same year, she was a writer-in-residence at the University of California, Berkeley, and in the fall of 1997 she will hold a Tinker Grant at Columbia University. Her most recent novel is *Los Vigilantes*. *E. Luminata*, the novel from which the selection published in this issue of *Grand Street* was excerpted, will be published in the fall of 1997 by Lumen Books.

MARK FERREZ was born in Rio de Janeiro in 1843. After living in Paris as a child, he returned to Brazil in his late teens and studied photography with the German engineer and botanist, Franz Keller, before opening his own business, specializing in landscape and ship photography, in 1865. Ferrez accompanied the Emperor Dom Pedro II on numerous expeditions to the interior of Brazil and, in 1875, he accepted an invitation to serve as photographer of the Geologic Commission of the Empire of Brazil. More than two hundred of his photographs taken during the course of the Charles Frederick Hartt expedition were shown in 1877 at the Commission headquarters. Over subsequent decades, Ferrez photographed many of Brazil's principal cities, documenting railroads, monuments, bridges, plantations, Indian tribes, mining operations, waterworks, waterfalls, forests, rivers, ports, industrial installations, and the entire fleet of the Imperial Navy. He also obtained the rights to the Lumière cinematographic projection system and opened the Pathé Cinema in Rio. Ferrez's photography earned numerous awards, including gold medals at the 1876 Philadelphia Exhibition, the 1878 Paris Exhibition, and the 1879 Rio de Janeiro Exhibition. Ferrez died in Brazil in 1923.

COLA FRANZEN's recent translations include Alicia Borinsky's novel, *Mean Woman* (University of Nebraska Press), Jorge Guillén's poetry collection, *Seen and Remembered* (forthcoming from City Lights), and *Si Regreso/If I Go Back* (Cross-Cultural Communications), a bilingual collection of poems by Juan Cameron. She has also translated the work of Argentine writer Saúl Yurkievich and Federico García Lorca.

MARK FRIED is Program Development Officer for Democratic Rights in the Americas at OXFAM, Canada, and the translator of Eduardo Galeano's *Walking Words* and *Soccer in Sun and Shadow*.

EDUARDO GALEANO is the author of the three-volume collection *Memory of Fire*, *Open Veins of Latin America*, *The Book of Embraces*, *We Say No*, and *Walking Words*, among other works. His most recent book is *Soccer in Sun and Shadow*. He lives in Montevideo, Uruguay.

JOÃO GUIMARÃES ROSA was born in Minas Gerais, Brazil, in 1908. After graduating from medical school and running a private practice for three years in the town of Itaguara, he moved to a career with the Ministry of Foreign Affairs. He was serving as vice-consul in Hamburg, Germany, when Brazil broke diplomatic relations with Germany, and was interned for four months in Baden-Baden. Over the following two decades, he held positions at the Brazilian embassies in Bogotá and Paris and was the cabinet chief of the Ministry of Foreign Affairs.

He was elected to the Brazilian Academy of Letters on November 16, 1967, three days before he died of a heart attack. One of the most important Brazilian writers of the twentieth century, he authored a novel, *Grande Sertão* (1956), and several collections of stories, including *Sagarana* (1946), *Corpo de Baile* (1956), *Primeiras Estórias* (1962), *Estas Estórias* (1969), and *Tutaméia: Terceiras Estórias* (1967), in which *Those Lopes* appeared in Portuguese.

LILIANA HEKER was born in Argentina. She won the International Casa des las Americas prize for her first collection of stories, *Those Who Beheld the Burning Bush*. In the 1970s, Heker founded the magazine, *El Ornitorrinco*, the only magazine to escape censorship by the military dictatorship. She is the author of several collections of stories, a novella, and a prize-winning novel. A volume of her selected stories, *The Stolen Party* (Coach House), was published in Canada in 1993. She lives in Buenos Aires.

KURT HOLLANDER, originally from New York City, has spent the last eight years in Mexico City, where he is the editor of *Poliester*, a contemporary art magazine on the Americas, and the owner of Billares Americo, a pool hall. He is currently working on a campaign book to be titled *Super Barrio for President*, which will be published by the New Press in 1998.

DOLORES M. KOCH was born in Havana, Cuba. She has translated Reinaldo Arenas's short stories for *The Penguin Book of International Gay Writing* and *Index on Censorship*, his novel, *The Doorman* (Grove Press), and his memoir, *Before Night Falls* (Viking). She has also translated Emily

Shindler's memoir, *Where Light and Shadow Meet* (W. W. Norton), and a novel by Colombian author Laura Restrepo, *Dulce compañía*, which will be published by HarperCollins in 1998. She holds a doctorate in Spanish American Literature.

PEDRO LEMEBEL was born in Santiago, Chile, in the mid-1950s. In 1987, along with Francisco Casas, he created the arts collective known as Yeguas del Apocalipsis, a group that has developed an extensive body of work in the plastic arts, including photography, video, performance art, and installations. His published works include *Incontables* (Editorial Ergo Sum), *La esquina es mi corazón* (Editorial Cuarto Propio), from which the two *crónicas* published in this issue of *Grand Street* were excerpted, and *Loco Afán, crónicas de sidario* (Editorial Lom). His articles have appeared in newspapers and magazines in Chile and internationally. He produces *Cancionero*, a radio program for Radio Tierra and lives in Santiago.

SUZANNE JILL LEVINE teaches at the University of California, Santa Barbara, and is currently a Guggenheim Fellow, writing a literary biography of Argentine author Manuel Puig, which will be published by Farrar, Straus & Giroux. She is also coediting, with Eliot Weinberger, *The Collected Essays of Jorge Luis Borges* (forthcoming from Viking).

JOSÉ LEZAMA LIMA was born in Cuba in 1912. Considered among the most influential figures of the Latin American avant-garde, he published several volumes of essays and poetry, as well as the novel *Paradiso*, which was translated into

English by Gregory Rabassa. Lezama Lima died in 1975. *The Fragments Drawn by Charm*, the collection from which the poems in this issue of *Grand Street* were excerpted, was published posthumously in 1978.

ENRIQUE LIHN was born in Santiago, Chile, in 1929. Although he started out as a painter, he eventually abandoned visual art for poetry. He was also well known as a novelist and a playwright, and he taught literature at the University of Chile. His poetry written during the years when Chile was governed by a military junta dealt increasingly with the social and human cost of dictatorship. The poems published in this issue of *Grand Street* were taken from his *Diario de Muerte*, a collection of fifty-four poems written during the six-week period in 1988 before Lihn died of cancer.

NATHANIEL MACKEY is the author of four chapbooks of poetry, *Four for Trane* (Golemics), *Septet for the End of Time* (Boneset), *Outlantish* (Chax Press), and *Song of the Andoumboulou: 18–20* (Moving Parts Press), and two books of poetry, *Eroding Witness* (University of Illinois Press) and *School of Udhra* (City Lights Books). *Strick: Song of the Andoumboulou 16–25*, a compact disc recording of poems read with musical accompaniment, was released in 1995 by Spoken Engine Company. Mackey is writing an ongoing prose composition, *From a Broken Bottle Traces of Perfume Still Emanate*, of which two volumes have been published: *Bedouin Hornbook* (Callaloo Fiction Series) and *Djbot Bahostus's Run* (Sun & Moon Press). He is the editor of the literary magazine *Hambone* and coeditor of the anthology *Moment's Notice: Jazz in Poetry and Prose* (Coffee

House Press). He is a professor of Literature at the University of California, Santa Cruz.

ALBERTO MANGUEL is a Canadian writer, born in Buenos Aires. He has translated a selection of Liliana Heker's stories titled *The Stolen Party* (Coach House). Manguel's most recent book is *A History of Reading* (Viking).

JOÃO CABRAL DE MELO NETO was born in Recife, Brazil, in 1920. He spent his childhood on his family's sugar plantations, and much of his later work described the subhuman living conditions of northeast Brazil's sugarcane workers. He moved to Rio de Janeiro in 1942, the year he published his first book of poems, *Pedra do Sono*. He joined Brazil's diplomatic service in 1945 and held numerous posts in Europe, Africa, and Latin America before becoming an ambassador—to Senegal and Honduras, among other countries—in 1972. He has published more than two dozen collections of poetry, including *Quaderna* (1960), *A Educação pela Pedra* (1966), *Museu de Tudo* (1975), *A Escola das Facas* (1980), *Auto do Frade* (1983), and *Agrestes* (1985). He retired to Rio de Janeiro in 1987.

GABRIELA MISTRAL was born Lucila Godoy Alcayaga, in Vicuña, Chile, in 1889. In 1908, she began using the pen name Gabriela Mistral and became a regular contributor to several literary magazines. She spent the next two decades working in the public school system and, in 1922, she was invited by the president of Mexico to collaborate in that country's educational reform. Her first book of poetry, *Desolación*, was published in 1922, and her second, *Ternura: Canciones de niños*, in 1924. In 1925, she was named the Chilean delegate to the Institute for Intellectual Cooperation of the League of Nations. In 1932, she began a career as consul of Chile, serving subsequently in Guatemala, Nice, Lisbon, Paris, Veracruz, and Brazil. In 1938, her third book of poems, *Tala*, was published by Sur. In 1945, Mistral became the first Spanish-American writer to be awarded the Nobel Prize for Literature. In 1951, she received the Chilean National Prize for Literature. She died in 1957 in Hempstead, New York, where she had stayed while representing Chile at the General Assembly of the United Nations. Her *Poema de Chile* was published posthumously in 1967.

FRED MOTEN lives in Los Angeles and teaches at the University of California, Santa Barbara. He writes about sound and music in literature and visual art.

FATIMA MUJČINOVIČ is a PhD student of Comparative Literature at the University of California, Santa Barbara. She was born and raised in Sarajevo, Bosnia, and has lived in the United States for three years. Several collections of her poetry translations have been published in the United States and Europe.

MARY ANN NEWMAN is a translator of Catalan and Spanish who lives in New York (and, sometimes, Barcelona). She has translated books by Quim Monzó and Xavier Rubert de Ventós.

RUBÉN ORTIZ-TORRES was born in Mexico City in 1964, and commutes between Mexico City and Los Angeles. He has a BFA from the Academy of San Carlos (ENAP) in Mexico City and a MFA from CalArts in Valencia, California.

His work is represented by Jan Kesner Gallery in Los Angeles and by the OMR Gallery in Mexico City. He has participated in several international exhibitions and film festivals, and work of his is currently in the collections of the Museum of Modern Art, New York, The Metropolitan Museum of Art, New York, the California Museum of Photography, Riverside, the Centro Cultural de Arte Contemporaneo, Mexico City, and the Museo Nacional Centro de Arte Reina Sofía, Madrid.

OCTAVIO PAZ was born in Mexico City in 1914. After World War II, he entered the Mexican diplomatic service and was posted to Japan and India. In 1968, he resigned as ambassador to India to protest his government's repressive brutality against demonstrators in Mexico City. He has taught at Cambridge and Harvard Universities, and received the Nobel Prize for Literature in 1990. His most recent works in English translation are the prose collections, *The Double Flame: Love and Eroticism* and *In Light of India* (both Harcourt Brace), and a selection of his poems from India, *A Tale of Two Gardens* (New Directions). Eleven of the projected fifteen volumes of his *Complete Works* have now been published in Spain and Mexico.

ALEJANDRA PIZARNIK was born in Buenos Aires in 1936. She is the author of several poetry collections, including *La tierra más ajena* (1955), *La última inocencia* (1956), *Las aventuras perdidas* (1958), *Arbol de Diana* (1962), *Los Trabajos y las Noches* (1965), which won the First Prize in the Buenos Aires Municipal Poetry Awards, and *Extracción de la piedra de la locura* (1968). She is also the author of several essays, including *La poesía de*

Octavio Paz and *El otro cielo de Julio Cortázar*. In 1968, she was awarded a Guggenheim Fellowship. She died in 1972.

HORACIO QUIROGA was born in Salto, Uruguay, in 1878. In 1891, his family moved to Montevideo and, in 1900, he traveled to Paris, where he met Darío, leader of the modernist movement in Spanish America. When he returned to Montevideo, he and his friends founded the first Uruguayan modernist literary circle. The following year, Quiroga published his first book, *Los arrecifes de coral*, a collection of poetry and prose. His second book, *El crimen del otro*, appeared in 1904 and, in 1905, he published *Los perseguidos*, a novella about madness. In 1906, he purchased a tract of virgin jungle in San Ignacio, Misiones, where he constructed his own house, devised a machine to kill ants and a furnace for making charcoal, as well as distilling orange liqueur from the fruit he grew. In 1915, exhausted by life in the wilderness, his wife committed suicide, leaving Quiroga to raise their two young children. Over the next ten years, he published several books, including two short-story collections, *Cuentos de amor, de locura y de muerte* and *Los desterrados*, and the children's collection, *Cuentos de la selva*. In 1917, Quiroga secured a position in the Uruguayan consulate in Buenos Aires. He remarried in 1927, and returned to San Ignacio with his second wife in 1932, when he was able to transfer his consul post there. The Uruguayan government abruptly closed its San Ignacio consulate two years later, leaving Quiroga with no salary. Abandoned by his wife and their young child, Quiroga began to suffer from prostate cancer. He committed suicide in 1937, six months after his admittance

to a hospital in Buenos Aires. *The Little Red Devil* appeared in Spanish in *Todos los cuentos (edición crítica)* (CEP de la Biblioteca Nacional, Madrid).

GREGORY RABASSA is the translator of Gabriel García Márquez's *One Hundred Years of Solitude*, and has also translated other major works by Latin American writers including Jorge Amado, Julio Cortázar, José Lezama Lima, Clarice Lispector, and Luis Rafael Sánchez. He has just completed translations of *Bras Cubas* and *Quincas Borba* by Machado de Assis, which will be published by Oxford University Press.

ALASTAIR REID is a poet, prose writer, traveler, and translator. He has been a staff writer at *The New Yorker* since 1958. In addition to his own writing, he has translated the writings of many Latin American writers, Jorge Luis Borges and Pablo Neruda among them, and Latin America is his chosen wavelength.

EDWARD W. SAID teaches literature at Columbia University. His recent books include *Culture and Imperialism* (Alfred A. Knopf), *The Politics of Dispossession* (Pantheon), and *Representations of the Intellectual* (Pantheon).

DORIS SALCEDO is a sculptor, who lives and works in Bogotá, Colombia. Her work focuses on the physical memory of the sites and victims of acts of extreme violence in Colombia over the past fifty years. An exhibition of her sculpture is being organized jointly by the New Museum of Contemporary Art in New York and Site Santa Fe for 1998. Her work has been shown in *Distemper: Dissonant Themes in the Art of the 1990s*, Hirshhorn Museum and Sculpture Garden, Washington,

D.C., 1996, *Doris Salcedo*, Le Creux de l'Enfer, Thiers, 1996, *About Place: Recent Art of the Americas*, Art Institute of Chicago, 1995, 1995 Carnegie International, Pittsburgh, and *Cocido y Crudo*, Museo Nacional Centro de Arte Reina Sofía, Madrid, 1994. She was awarded a Penny McCall Foundation Grant in 1993 and a Guggenheim Foundation Grant in 1995.

LUIS RAFAEL SÁNCHEZ was born in Humacao, Puerto Rico, in 1936. He studied theater arts at the University of Puerto Rico and Columbia University, received a master's degree in Spanish literature from New York University in 1963 and a PhD from Universidad Complutense de Madrid in 1976. A playwright, novelist, and essayist, Sánchez has published several plays, including *La pasión según Antígona Pérez* (Cultural, Puerto Rico) and *Quintuples* (Ediciones del Norte). His novel, *La guaracha del Macho Camacho* (De La Flor), was published in Argentina, Spain, and Cuba, and has been translated into English, French, and Portuguese. A collection of essays, *La Guagua Aerea* (Cultural, Puerto Rico), was published in 1994. He currently teaches Spanish literature at the City College of New York. His story, *Hum!*, appeared in Spanish in his collection *En cuerpo de camisa* (Editorial Cultural, Puerto Rico).

MARK SCHAFER is a literary translator and visual artist living in Boston. He has translated a wide range of Latin American authors in a variety of genres, among them the novelists Alberto Ruy Sánchez and Virilio Piñera, the poets Gloria Gervitz and Alberto Blanco, and the essayists José Lezama Lima and Julio Ortega. His collection of stories by Jesús Gardea, *Stripping Away the Sorrows from this World*, will be published this year by Editorial Aldus, S.A. He is currently translating Alberto Ruy Sánchez's latest novel, tentatively titled *Between the Lips of Water*.

PAUL SEESEQUASIS is a mixed-blood Cree writer, who lives and works in Toronto, Canada. He has just completed his first novel, *Indian Wars*.

PETER SELLARS has directed more than a hundred theater and opera productions in the United States and abroad. A graduate of Harvard University, he studied in Japan, China, and India before becoming the Artistic Director of the Boston Shakespeare Company. At twenty-six, he was appointed Director of the American National Theater at the Kennedy Center in Washington, D.C. A frequent guest at the Salzburg and Glyndebourne Festivals, he has specialized in directing contemporary operas, most notably Olivier Messiaen's *St. François d'Assise* and John Adams and Alice Goodman's *Nixon in China* and *The Death of Klinghoffer*. His production of *The Rake's Progress* was performed at the Théâtre du Châtelet in Paris in 1996. Sellars was the Artistic Director of the 1990 and 1993 Los Angeles Festivals and is a Professor of World Arts and Cultures at the University of California, Los Angeles. He is a recipient of the MacArthur Prize Fellowship.

LUIS SEPÚLVEDA was born in northern Chile in 1949. Forced to leave Chile due to his political activities in the students' movement, he founded theater groups in Peru, Ecuador, and Colombia, and worked for UNESCO and as a freelance journalist. Sepúlveda has won several literary awards, including the Casa de las Americas in 1969. He acquired international fame with his novel, *Un viejo que leía novelas de amor* (Ediciones

Júcar, 1989), which was published in English as *The Old Man Who Read Love Stories* (Helen & Kurt Wolff/Harcourt Brace) in 1994. He is currently working on two novels and a book about Patagonia's railways. He has been living in Hamburg, Germany, since 1980.

ROSE M. SEVILLANO received her master's degree in Spanish Literature from Hunter College, and currently teaches Spanish to Spanish-speaking students at Roosevelt High School in Yonkers, New York. She lives in the Bronx, New York.

REGINALD SHEPHERD's first book, *Some Are Drowning* (University of Pittsburgh), won the 1993 AWP Award. His second book, *Angel, Interrupted* (University of Pittsburgh), was published in 1996. A recipient of the 1993 "Discovery"/*The Nation* award and a 1995 NEA Fellowship, among other honors, Shepherd lives in Chicago and teaches at Northern Illinois University. "From the World of Matter" is part of the manuscript of a third collection of poems entitled *Wrong*.

CAROL SQUIERS is a writer, editor, and curator who lives in New York City. She is currently senior editor of *American Photo* magazine and a regular contributor to *Artforum*. She has written for a variety of publications, including *The New York Times, Vogue, Vanity Fair, The Village Voice,* and *Aperture*. She is currently working on a revised edition of *The Critical Image: Essays on Contemporary Photography*, a collection of articles by writers including Rosalind Krauss, Simon Watney, and Abigail Solomon-Godeau.

ROBERTO TEJADA has lived and worked in Mexico City since 1987. He currently edits the English-Spanish journal *Mandorla: New Writing from the Americas*, an annual of advanced poetry and poetics. His poems have been featured in *Sulfur, O.blek, apex of the M, Trafika,* and *Tyuonyi*, as well as in *The Gertrude Stein Awards in Innovative American Poetry 1993–1994* and *The Best American Poetry 1996*. Most recently he wrote the introductory essay to *Images of the Spirit: Photographs by Graciela Iturbide* (Aperture Books).

ANN TEMKIN is the Muriel and Philip Berman Curator of Twentieth-Century Art at the Philadelphia Museum of Art.

ROBERT VANDERMOLEN lives and works as a painting contractor in Grand Rapids, Michigan. He received a NEA Fellowship for 1995. His six collections of poetry include *Along the River and Circumstances*, the chapbook *Of Pines*, and the chaplet *Night Weather*, and recent poems have appeared in *Epoch, Sulfur, House Organ, Mudfish,* and *Artful Dodge*. His new collection, *Peaches*, will be published by Sky Press in June 1997.

WILLIAM T. VOLLMANN is working on a study of the ethics of violence.

WENDY WATRISS is a photographer, curator, and writer. She is one of the founders of FotoFest, a photographic arts and education organization based in Houston, Texas, and has served as its artistic director since 1991. Her photographic work has been exhibited around the world, and she is the recipient of awards and grants from the National Endowment for the

Humanities, the Rockefeller Foundation, and the National Endowment for the Arts/Mid-Atlantic Arts Alliance, among others. In 1992, Watriss coordinated a series of exhibits on Latin American photography for Independent Curators Inc., entitled *Image and Memory: Latin American Photography from 1880 to 1992*. A book based on these exhibitions will be published by University of Texas Press in the fall of 1997.

ELIOT WEINBERGER's essays are collected in *Works on Paper, Outside Stories* (both New Directions), and *Written Reaction* (Marsilio). He is an editor of *American Poetry Since 1950: Innovators & Outsiders* (Marsilio), and the translator of many books of Latin American poetry and prose.

JAMES WELLING was born in Hartford, Connecticut, in 1951. Solo exhibitions of his recent *Light Sources* series have been held at Jay Gorney Modern Art, New York, S. L. Simpson Gallery, Toronto, and Galerie Xavier Hufkehs, Brussels. His photographs, *Railroad Towns*, were seen at Documenta IX in Kassel. He is the head of the Department of Photography at the University of California, Los Angeles. He lives and works in Los Angeles and New York, and is represented by Jay Gorney Modern Art, New York.

GARRETT WHITE is the translator of Blaise Cendrars's *Hollywood: Mecca of the Movies* (University of California Press). His translation of *Christ With A Switchblade: Selected Writings of Luis Buñuel* will be published by the University of California Press in 1998. He lives in Hollywood, where he works as a writer and film journalist.

OCTAVIO ZAYA is an art critic and independent curator, who has been based in New York since 1978. He is an associate editor of *Atlántica*, the bilingual publication of the Centro Atlántico de Arte Moderno, Canary Islands, a consulting editor of NKA *Journal of Contemporary African Art*, New York, and a correspondent for *Flash Art*, Milan. He is currently co-curating, with Nigerian critic Okwui Enwezor, *Alternating Currents*, the main event at the second Johannesburg Biennale.

RICHARD ZENITH is a translator, poet, and critic. His translations include *113 Galician-Portuguese Troubadour Poems*, Fernando Pessoa's *The Book of Disquietude*, and several novels by António Lobo Antunes. He lives in Lisbon.

Grand Street would like to thank the following for their generous support:

EDWARD LEE CAVE
CATHY AND STEPHEN GRAHAM
BARBARA HOWARD
DOMINIC MAN-KIT LAM
THE NEW YORK STATE COUNCIL ON THE ARTS
SUZANNE AND SANFORD J. SCHLESINGER
BETTY AND STANLEY K. SHEINBAUM

You've heard about
SHENANDOAH
for years.
Why not subscribe today
and really get to know us?

(We'll send you a free 5" x 7" broadside featuring a complete poem
by a *Shenandoah* contributor to sweeten the deal!)

Betty Adcock, Neal Bowers, Fred Chappell, Philip Dacey, Brendan Galvin, Seamus Heaney, William ~~~~~, Andrew Hudgins, William Matthews, Jeanne Murray Wal~~ ~~igley, Carolyn Kizer, Larry Rivers, Reynolds Price, John ~~ ~~icholas Delbanco, Kent Nelson, Margaret Gibson, A. Man~~~ ~~Rodney Jones, Charles Wright, Molly Best Ti~~~~~ ~~orah Pope, David Borofka, Ruth Padel, W. S. Merw~~ ~~Albert Goldb~~ ~~Harry Humes, Colette Inex, William~~ ~~nne Boruch, Rachel Hadas, Rebecca ~~ ~~laser, Mary Oliver, Katherine Sonia~~ ~~Katherine Stripling Byer, Hayden ~~ ~~ichael Longley, Scott Russell Sander~~ ~~ly, Robert Hill

Shenandoah seems about the best bargain in literature that one could possibly find these days. It is just as sleek and thick as journals twice its price, and has more beauty and life between its covers than anything I have read in a long time.

-- *Literary Magazine Review*

SHENANDOAH

Washington and Lee University / Troubadour Theater, 2nd Floor
Box EX-A(B) / Lexington, Virginia 24450-0303

Name_____

                                                               GS

Address_____

City, State, Zip _____

Single issue: $5.00   Subscription: $28 / 2 years
                                                    $15 / 1 year

ILLUSTRATIONS

FRONT COVER
Tatiana Parcero, *Interior Cartography #36*, 1996. Black-and-white photograph on acetate and C-print, 10 x 8 in. The map superimposed on the hand in this work is taken from a series of Aztec charts or "codices," believed to date from the sixteenth century, that were made with native pigments on handmade *amate* paper by native scribes, after the Spanish Conquest, in order to supply the government with a wide range of information about Aztec culture, including local community structures and history. Courtesy of the artist and Carla Stellweg Gallery, New York.

BACK COVER
Rubén Ortiz-Torres, *Los Payasos Diabólicos/The Devil Clowns*, Tijuana, Mexico, 1991. Fuji superglossy C-print, 20 x 24 in. Courtesy of the artist and Jan Kesner Gallery, Los Angeles.

TITLE PAGE
James Welling, *High Rollers Lounge, Pittsburgh, PA; 1993*. Gelatin silver print. Courtesy of the artist and Jay Gorney Gallery, New York.

TABLE OF CONTENTS
Marc Ferrez, *Entrance to Rio de Janeiro (View from Outside the Bay)*, circa 1880. Albumen print, 9 3/4 x 19 1/2 in. Courtesy of Hack Hoffenberg.

PP. 25–32 Rubén Ortiz-Torres, *Hall of Mirrors*. Seven Fuji superglossy C-prints, 20 x 24 in. Titles and dates appear with images. Courtesy of the artist and Jan Kesner Gallery, Los Angeles.

P. 34 Photograph courtesy of AP/Wide World Photos.

P. 36 (TOP) From *La Verdadera Historia del Chupacabras*, (San Juan, Puerto Rico: Redacción Noticiosa, 1996). **(BOTTOM)** Photograph courtesy of AP/Wide World Photos.

P. 56 Collage by Mary Anne Barkhouse.

PP. 73–80 Doris Salcedo, *Unland*. Titles and dates appear with images. **P. 73** Wood, cement, cloth, and steel, 77 1/2 x 47 1/4 x 74 in. Courtesy of the Hirshhorn Museum and Sculpture Garden, Smithsonian Institution, Washington, D.C., Joseph H. Hirshhorn Purchase Fund, 1995. Photograph by Lee Stalsworth. **PP. 74–75** Installation view, 1995 Carnegie International, the Carnegie Museum of Art, Pittsburgh, Pennsylvania. Photograph by Richard Stoner. **P. 76** Wood, cement, cloth, glass, and steel, 64 3/4 x 39 1/4 x 14 1/2 in. Courtesy of the Caldic Collection, Rotterdam. Photograph by Orcutt & Van Der Putten. **P. 77** Wood, cement, and metal, 45 x 73 1/2 x 20 in. Collection of the Carnegie Museum of Art, Pittsburgh. Photograph by D. James Dee. **P. 78** Wood, cement, steel, glass, and cloth, 110 x 47 x 14 1/2 in. Private collection. Photograph by Orcutt & Van Der Putten. **P. 79** Wood, fabric, and bone, 102 1/2 x 18 1/4 x 13 in. Private collection. Photograph by Lee Stalsworth. **P. 80** Wall installation with three niches. Drywall, 6 shoes, cow bladder, and surgical thread, 36 x 58 in. Photograph by D. James Dee. All photographs except **P. 73** courtesy of the artist and Alexander and Bonin, New York.

PP. 121–128 *Paradise.* A portfolio of eleven artworks. Artists, titles, and dates appear with images. **P. 121** Color photograph documenting earth/body work with flowers on rocks, El Yagul, Oaxaca, Mexico, 20 x 16 in. Courtesy of the Estate of Ana Mendieta and Galerie Lelong, New York. **P. 122** Black-and-white silver print, edition of 2 with 1 A.P., 50 x 40 in. Courtesy of the artist and Angles Gallery, Santa Monica, California. **P. 123 (TOP)** Mixed media, 37 1/2 x 97 1/2 x 67 1/2 in. Courtesy of the artist and Basilico Fine Arts, New York. **P. 123 (BOTTOM)** Mixed media, 24 x 100 x 43 in. Courtesy of the artist and Steinbaum Krauss Gallery, New York. **P. 124** Installation at the Fabric Workshop, Philadelphia, 1992. Video monitors, computers, multi-dimensional fractal modeling program, Sheetrock, and wood. Courtesy of the artist and the Fabric Workshop. Photograph by Will Brown. **P. 125 (TOP)** Cibachrome, 12 1/2 x 18 3/4 in. Courtesy of the artist and Marian Goodman Gallery, New York. **P. 125 (BOTTOM)** Installation at Deitch Projects, New York, 1996. Mixed media. Courtesy of the artist and Deitch Projects. **P. 126** C-print, edition of 3, 60 x 40 in. Courtesy of the artists and Xavier LaBoulbenne Gallery, New York. **P. 127 (TOP)** Color photograph with polyester resin over wooden framework, 30 x 40 in. Courtesy of the artist and OMR Gallery, Mexico City. **P. 127 (BOTTOM)** Video installation. Courtesy of the artist and Valenzuela & Klenner Gallery, Bogotá, Colombia. **P. 128** Polyethylene, wood, plexiglass, sand, vegetables, and live snails, 31 1/2 x 15 3/4 x 15 3/4 in. Courtesy of the artist and Ruth Benzacar Gallery, Buenos Aires. Photograph by Pedro Roth.

PP. 161–168 James Welling, *Railroad Towns.* Seven gelatin silver prints. Titles and dates appear with images. Courtesy of the artist and Jay Gorney Gallery, New York.

P. 196–197 AND P. 200–201 Photographs courtesy of the Cornerstone Theater Company, Los Angeles.

P. 205 Courtesy of the Théâtre du Châtelet, Paris. Photograph by Marie-Noëlle Robert.

PP. 209–216 *Navigation.* A portfolio of twelve artworks. Artists, titles, and dates appear with images. **P. 209** Black-and-white photograph on acetate and C-print, 10 x 8 in. Courtesy of the artist and Carla Stellweg Gallery, New York.

P. 210 (TOP) Performance with live fleas at the Fabric Workshop, Philadelphia, 1996. Courtesy of the artist and the Fabric Workshop. **P. 210 (BOTTOM)** From the installation *Deviations in Space, Various Virgins* at David Zwirner Gallery, New York, 1997. Metal, iron, foam, and plastic, approximately 90 x 90 x 30 in., edition of 5. Courtesy of the artist and David Zwirner Gallery. **P. 211** Paint on pleated cardboard on canvas with pushpins, 46 x 46 in. Courtesy of the artist and John Weber Gallery, New York. **P. 212 (LEFT)** Mixed media, 89 x 56 3/4 x 32 3/8 in. Courtesy of the artist and L.A. Louver Gallery, Venice, California. **P. 212 (RIGHT)** Installation view from the exhibition *Interzones*, Künstforeningen, Copenhagen, 1996. **P. 213** Paint, stitching, feather, and photo silk screen on one section of non-woven fabric, 82 1/2 x 55 1/4 in. Courtesy of the artist and Alexander and Bonin, New York. **P. 214 (TOP)** From *The Children of Peter Pan*, 1995. Thirty-seven vintage children's garments, hangers, and painted map of Cuba. Courtesy of the artist. **P. 214 (BOTTOM)** A series of interactive and mobile installations placed in independent New York City taxis between February 7 and March 8, 1997. Courtesy of the artist and Ronald Feldman Fine Arts, New York. **P. 215** Mark Dion, installation at De Vleeshal, Middelburg, Holland, 1995. Boat, sand, canvas, fan, and mixed media on wood platform. Courtesy of the artist and American Fine Arts, Co., New York. **P. 216 (TOP)** Documentary film still. Courtesy of the artist and Valenzuela & Klenner Gallery, Bogotá, Colombia. **P. 216 (BOTTOM)** Black-and-white photograph from the *Malecón* series. Courtesy of the artist and Art in General, New York.

P. 232 (LEFT) Albumen silver print from glass negative by François Aubert, 14 1/8 x 10 1/8 in. Courtesy of the Gilman Paper Company, New York. **(RIGHT)** Albumen silver print from glass negative by François Aubert, 13 3/16 x 10 15/16 in. Courtesy of the Gilman Paper Company, New York.

P. 236–246 Marc Ferrez, *Views of Brazil.* Eight albumen prints. Descriptions and dates appear with images. **PP. 236–237** 11 3/8 x 15 1/4 in. **P. 238** 11 1/4 x 15 1/8 in. **P. 239** 11 1/4 x 15 3/8 in. **P. 240–241** 11 1/4 x 15 1/4 in. **P. 242** 9 3/4 x 19 1/2 in. **P. 243** 9 3/4 x 19 1/2 in. **P. 244** 11 5/16 x 15 5/16 in. **P. 246** 9 3/4 x 19 1/2 in. Courtesy of Hack Hoffenberg.

Subscribe to "the leading intellectual forum in the US"

—*New York* magazine

Since we began publishing in 1963, *The New York Review of Books* has provided remarkable variety and intellectual excitement. Twenty times a year, the world's best writers and scholars address themselves to 130,000 discerning readers worldwide…people who know that the widest range of subjects—literature, art, politics, science, history, music, education—will be discussed with wit, clarity, and brilliance.

In each issue subscribers of *The New York Review* enjoy articles by such celebrated writers as John Updike, Elizabeth Hardwick, Gore Vidal, Nadine Gordimer, Oliver Sacks, and countless others, as well as the literary bare-knuckle boxing of the Letters to the Editors section.

If you think you too might enjoy the penetrating insights and arguments found in each issue of *The New York Review*, subscribe now with this special introductory offer. You'll not only save over 60% ($42.50) from the newsstand price, but you'll also get a free copy of *Selections*. With this offer you'll receive:

➤ **20 Issues** A full year's subscription of 20 issues for just $27.50—a saving of 50% off the regular subscription rate of $55.00 and a saving of $42.50 (60%) off the newsstand price.

➤ **A Free Book:** *Selections* is a collection of 19 reviews and essays published verbatim from our first two issues. In it you'll discover how certain works such as *The Naked Lunch* or *The Fire Next Time*, now regarded as modern classics, were initially perceived by critics when they were first published and reviewed.

➤ **A Risk-Free Guarantee** If you are unhappy with your subscription at any time, you may cancel. We will refund the unused portion of the subscription cost. What's more, *Selections* is yours to keep as our gift to you for trying *The New York Review*.

The New York Review of Books

Return to: Subscriber Service Dept., PO Box 420382, Palm Coast, FL 32142-0382

❑ **Yes!** Please enter my one-year subscription (20 issues) to *The New York Review* at the special introductory rate of only $27.50 (a saving of 60% off the newsstand rate). With my paid subscription, I will also receive *Selections* at no extra charge and a no-risk guarantee.

❑ $27.50 enclosed*   Charge my: ❑ Am Ex ❑ MasterCard ❑ Visa ❑ Bill me. (US only)

Name _____

Address _____

_____

City/State/Zip _____

A7F17G

Credit Card Number _____

Credit Card Expiration Date/Signature _____

SELECTIONS

FREE with this offer

☎ **For faster service on credit card orders, fax to:** (212) 586-8003. Please include your own phone and fax in case of questions. *If you fax this order, do not also mail it.*

*Make checks or US money orders payable to *The New York Review of Books*. We accept US Dollars drawn on a US bank or Canadian Dollars drawn on a Canadian bank. If paying by CDN$ return to Mike Johnson, *The New York Review of Books*, 1755 Broadway, 5th Floor, New York, NY 10019-3780. We cannot accept international money orders. Rates outside the US: to Canada $53/$72.50CDN, Rest of World Regular Post $57, Rest of World Print Flow Air Post (recommended for Africa, Australia, the Far East, New Zealand, and South America) $84. Credit card orders will be charged at the US Dollar rates shown. Please allow 6 to 8 weeks for delivery of your first issue.

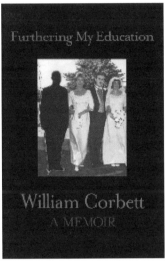

THE
American Voice

No. 44

New Voices from Latin America & Spain

Marjorie Agosín
GUEST EDITOR

featuring
Ana Pizarro, Belen Gopegui,
Daisy Zamora, Ruth Behar, Maria Sanz,
Giovanna Pollarolo, Laura Riesco,
Claudia Roquette-Pinto, Elena Santiago,
Paz Molina, Ana Maria Rodriguez,
Mercedes Escolano, Claudia Bernardi,
Cristina Peri Rossi, Denise Emmer,
Matilde Salganicoff and many more.

**AVAILABLE AT BOOKSTORES
OR BY SUBSCRIPTION ($15)**

THE
American Voice
**332 WEST BROADWAY
LOUISVILLE, KENTUCKY 40202 USA**

FREDERICK SMOCK, EDITOR

GRAND STREET
BACK ISSUES
COLLECT THEM NOW

Edward Said on Jean Genet; Terry Southern & Dennis Hopper on Larry Flynt
STORIES: Elizabeth Bishop, William T. Vollmann; PORTFOLIOS: William Eggleston, Saul Steinberg; POEMS: John Ashbery, Bei Dao.

36

William S. Burroughs on guns; John Kenneth Galbraith on JFK's election
STORIES: Pierrette Fleutiaux, Eduardo Galeano; PORTFOLIOS: *Blackboard Equations*, John McIntosh; POEMS: Clark Coolidge, Suzanne Gardinier.

37

Kazuo Ishiguro & Kenzaburo Oe on Japanese literature; Julio Cortázar's HOPSCOTCH: A Lost Chapter
STORIES: Fernando Pessoa, Ben Sonnenberg; PORTFOLIOS: Linda Connor, Robert Rauschenberg; POEMS: Jimmy Santiago Baca, Charles Wright.

38

Nadine Gordimer: SAFE HOUSES; James Miller on Michel Foucault
STORIES: Hervé Guibert, Dubravka Ugrešić; PORTFOLIOS: *Homicide: Bugsy Siegel*, Mark di Suvero; POEMS: Amiri Baraka, Michael Palmer.

39

Gary Giddins on Dizzy Gillespie; Toni Morrison on race and literature
STORIES: Yehudit Katzir, Marcel Proust; PORTFOLIOS: Gretchen Bender, Brice Marden; POEMS: Arkadii Dragomoshchenko, Tom Paulin.

40

AVAILABLE NOW

Nina Berberova on the Turgenev Library; Mary-Claire King on tracing "the disappeared"
STORIES: Ben Okri, Kurt Schwitters; PORTFOLIOS: Louise Bourgeois, Jean Tinguely; POEMS: Rae Armantrout, Eugenio Montale.

41

David Foster Wallace: THREE PROTRUSIONS; Henry Green: An unfinished novel
STORIES: Félix de Azúa, Eduardo Galeano; PORTFOLIOS: Sherrie Levine, Ariane Mnouchkine & Ingmar Bergman—two productions of Euripides; POEMS: Jorie Graham, Gary Snyder.

42

Jamaica Kincaid on the biography of a dress; Stephen Trombley on designing death machines
STORIES: Victor Erofeyev, Christa Wolf; PORTFOLIOS: Joseph Cornell, Sue Williams; POEMS: Robert Creeley, Kabir.

43

Martin Duberman on Stonewall; Andrew Kopkind: Slacking Toward Bethlehem
STORIES: Georges Perec, Edmund White; PORTFOLIOS: William Christenberry, Fred Wilson; POEMS: Lyn Hejinian, Sharon Olds.

44

John Cage: Correspondence; Roberto Lovato: Down and Out in Central L.A.
STORIES: David Gates, Duong Thu Huong; PORTFOLIOS: Ecke Bonk, Gerhard Richter; POEMS: A. R. Ammons, C. H. Sisson.

45

William T. Vollmann on the Navajo-Hopi Land Dispute; Ice-T, Easy-E: L.A. rappers get open with Brian Cross
STORIES: David Foster Wallace, Italo Calvino; PORTFOLIOS: Nancy Rubins, Dennis Balk; POEMS: Michael Palmer, Martial.

46

Untitled, 1929.   Untitled, 1930.

Magpie Magazine Gallery, Vancouver, CANADA

Newsstand, Bellingham, WA
Bailey Coy Books, Seattle, WA
Hideki Ohmori, Seattle, WA

Looking Glass Bookstore, Portland, OR
Powell's Books, Portland, OR
Reading Frenzy, Portland, OR

Baxter's Books, Minneapolis, MN
Minnesota Book Center, Minneapolis, MN
University of Minnesota Bookstore, Minneapolis, MN
Walker Art Center Bookshop, Minneapolis, MN
Hungry Mind Bookstore, St. Paul, MN
Odegard Books, St. Paul, MN

. . . On Sundays, Tokyo, JAPAN

ASUC Bookstore, Berkeley, CA
Black Oak Books, Berkeley, CA
Cody's Books, Berkeley, CA
Bookstore Fiona, Carson, CA
Huntley Bookstore, Claremont, CA
Book Soup, Hollywood, CA
University Bookstore, Irvine, CA
Museum of Contemporary Art, La Jolla, CA
UCSD Bookstore, La Jolla, CA
A.R.T. Press, Los Angeles, CA
Museum of Contemporary Art, Los Angeles, CA
Occidental College Bookstore, Los Angeles, CA
Sun & Moon Press Bookstore, Los Angeles, CA
UCLA/Armand Hammer Museum, Los Angeles, CA
Stanford Bookstore, Newark, CA
Diesel, A Bookstore, Oakland, CA
Blue Door Bookstore, San Diego, CA
Museum of Contemporary Art, San Diego, CA
The Booksmith, San Francisco, CA
City Lights, San Francisco, CA
Green Apple Books, San Francisco, CA
Modern Times Bookstore, San Francisco, CA
MuseumBooks–SF MOMA, San Francisco, CA
San Francisco Camerawork, San Francisco, CA
Logos, Santa Cruz, CA
Arcana, Santa Monica, CA
Midnight Special Bookstore, Santa Monica, CA
Reader's Books, Sonoma, CA
Small World Books, Venice, CA
Ventura Bookstore, Ventura, CA

Chinook Bookshop, Colorado Springs, CO
The Bookies, Denver, CO
Newsstand Cafe, Denver, CO
Tattered Cover Bookstore, Denver, CO
Stone Lion Bookstore, Fort Collins, CO

Nebraska Bookstore, Lincoln, NE

Asun Bookstore, Reno, NV

Sam Weller's Zion Bookstore, Salt Lake City, UT

Kansas Union Bookstore, Lawrence, KS
Terra Nova Bookstore, Lawrence, KS

Bookman's, Tucson, AZ

Bookworks, Albuquerque, NM
Page One Bookstore, Albuquerque, NM
Salt of the Earth, Albuquerque, NM
Cafe Allegro, Los Alamos, NM
Collected Works, Santa Fe, NM

Honolulu Book Shop, Honolulu, HI

Book People, Austin, TX
Bookstop, Austin, TX
University Co-op Society, Austin, TX
McKinney Avenue Contemporary Gift Shop, Dallas, TX
Bookstop, Houston, TX
Brazos Bookstore, Houston, TX
Contemporary Arts Museum Shop, Houston, TX
Diversebooks, Houston, TX
Menil Collection Bookstore, Houston, TX
Museum of Fine Arts, Houston, TX
Texas Gallery, Houston, TX
Bookstop, Plano, TX

Page One, SINGAPORE

Bookland of Brunswick, Brunswick, ME
University of Maine Bookstore, Orono, ME
Books Etc., Portland, ME
Raffles Cafe Bookstore, Portland, ME

Pages, Toronto, CANADA

Dartmouth Bookstore, Hanover, NH
Toadstool Bookshop, Peterborough, NH

Northshire Books, Manchester, VT

Wootton's Books, Amherst, MA
Boston University Bookstore, Boston, MA
Harvard Book Store, Cambridge, MA
M.I.T. Press Bookstore, Cambridge, MA
Cisco Harland Books, Marlborough, MA
Broadside Bookshop, Northampton, MA
Provincetown Bookshop, Provincetown, MA
Water Street Books, Williamstown, MA

Main Street News, Ann Arbor, MI
Shaman Drum Bookshop, Ann Arbor, MI
Cranbrook Art Museum Books, Bloomfield Hills, MI
Book Beat, Oak Park, MI

Afterwords, Milwaukee, WI

Farley's Bookshop, New Hope, PA
Faber Books, Philadelphia, PA
Waterstone's Booksellers, Philadelphia, PA
Andy Warhol Museum, Pittsburgh, PA
Encore Books, Mechanicsburg, PA
Encore Books, State College, PA

Accident or Design, Providence, RI
Brown University Bookstore, Providence, RI
College Hill Store, Providence, RI

Yale Cooperative, New Haven, CT
UConn Co-op, Storrs, CT

Rosetta News, Carbondale, IL
Pages for All Ages, Champaign, IL
Mayuba Bookstore, Chicago, IL
Museum of Contemporary Art, Chicago, IL
Seminary Co-op Bookstore, Chicago, IL

Indiana University Bookstore,
Bloomington, IN

UC Bookstore, Cincinnati, OH
Bank News, Cleveland, OH
Ohio State University Bookstore, Columbus, OH
Student Book Exchange, Columbus, OH
Books & Co., Dayton, OH
Kenyon College Bookstore, Gambier, OH
Oberlin Consumers Cooperative, Oberlin, OH

Encore Books, Princeton, NJ
Micawber Books, Princeton, NJ

Community Bookstore, Brooklyn, NY
Talking Leaves, Buffalo, NY
Colgate University Bookstore, Hamilton, NY
Book Revue, Huntington, NY
The Bookery, Ithaca, NY
A Different Light, New York, NY
Art Market, New York, NY
B. Dalton, New York, NY
Coliseum Books, New York, NY
Collegiate Booksellers, New York, NY
Doubleday Bookshops, New York, NY
Exit Art/First World Store, New York, NY
Gold Kiosk, New York, NY
Gotham Book Mart, New York, NY
Museum of Modern Art Bookstore, New York, NY
New York University Book Center, New York, NY
Posman Books, New York, NY
Rizzoli Bookstores, New York, NY
St. Mark's Bookshop, New York, NY
Shakespeare & Co., New York, NY
Spring Street Books, New York, NY
Wendell's Books, New York, NY
Whitney Museum of Modern Art, New York, NY
Syracuse University Bookstore, Syracuse, NY

Iowa Book & Supply, Iowa City, IA
Prairie Lights, Iowa City, IA
University Bookstore, Iowa City, IA

Box of Rocks, Bowling Green, KY
Carmichael's, Louisville, KY

Louie's Bookstore Cafe, Baltimore, MD

Xanadu Bookstore, Memphis, TN

Bridge Street Books, Washington, DC
Chapters, Washington, DC
Franz Bader Bookstore, Washington, DC
Olsson's, Washington, DC
Politics & Prose, Washington, DC

Daedalus Used Bookshop, Charlottesville, VA
Studio Art Shop, Charlottesville, VA
Williams Corner, Charlottesville, VA

Library Ltd., Clayton, MO
Whistler's Books, Kansas City, MO
Left Bank Books, St. Louis, MO

Paper Skyscraper, Charlotte, NC
Regulator Bookshop, Durham, NC

Chapter Two Bookstore, Charleston, SC
Intermezzo, Columbia, SC
Open Book, Greenville, SC

Square Books, Oxford, MS

Oxford Bookstore, Atlanta, GA

Books & Books, Coral Gables, FL
Goerings Book Center, Gainesville, FL
Bookstop, Miami, FL
Rex Art, Miami, FL
Inkwood Books, Tampa, FL

Lenny's News, New Orleans, LA

And at selected Barnes & Noble and Bookstar bookstores nationwide.

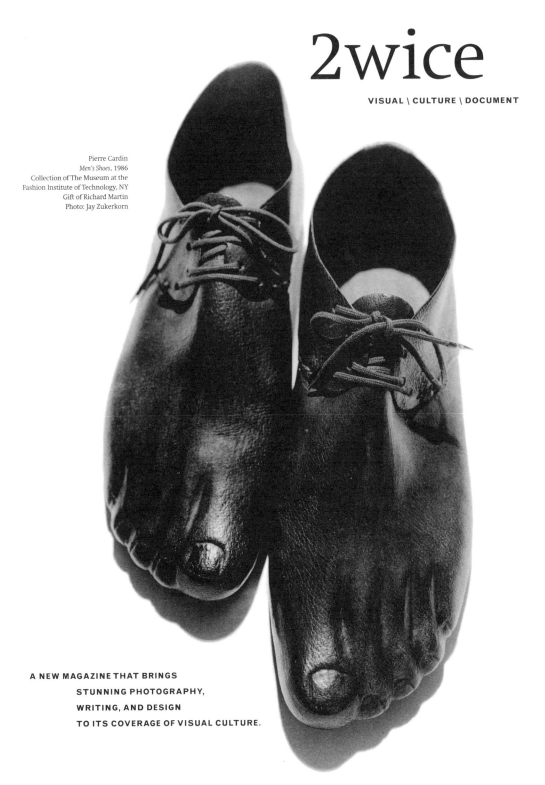

2wice

VISUAL \ CULTURE \ DOCUMENT

Pierre Cardin
Men's Shoes, 1986
Collection of The Museum at the
Fashion Institute of Technology, NY
Gift of Richard Martin
Photo: Jay Zukerkorn

A NEW MAGAZINE THAT BRINGS
STUNNING PHOTOGRAPHY,
WRITING, AND DESIGN
TO ITS COVERAGE OF VISUAL CULTURE.

ON SALE NOW. AVAILABLE AT FINE BOOKSTORES.

TO SUBSCRIBE : TEL : 212 228 0540 | FAX : 212 228 0654